The
BOY ENGINEER

By EDWARD L. THROM

A Popular Mechanics Book

Illustrated by EVELYN URBANOWICH
and ROBERT PIOUS

 GOLDEN PRESS · NEW YORK

Second Printing, 1960

Library of Congress Catalog Card Number: 59-14102

TABLE OF CONTENTS

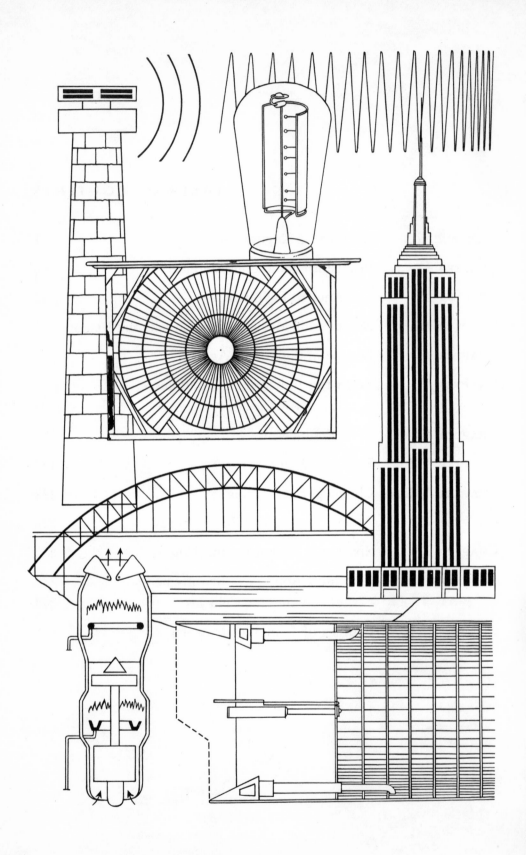

A CAREER IN ENGINEERING

YOU are interested in engineering—otherwise you would not have this book in your hands. It is our hope that you will be a great deal more interested before you put it down, because your country —whether it be the United States, Canada, Australia or any of the countries of the free world where these words will be read — needs young people who are genuinely interested in engineering.

For the next ten years—roughly the time required by most readers of this book to finish high school and college—the United States alone will need about 50,000 trained engineers to be ready to enter this field every year. Right now the country is training only about half that number.

Why do we need all these young engineers? For a number of vital reasons: to keep our country strong in the highly technical type of military defenses we need; to increase the production of our mines, mills and factories so that the needs of an expanding population can be met; to solve the problems of water shortages and traffic congestion and to help achieve cheaper sources of power, and the like.

All of these problems are engineering problems, and they will require engineers for their solution.

The nations of the free world are engaged in a fierce and real competition with nations ruled by dictators. The winners in this competition will be those governments which—while maintaining peace —supply their peoples with the highest standards of living. And in this age of technology, engineers are behind a large proportion of the advances in the standard of living.

In the United States, and in other free nations where a person may choose his life work, there is a shortage of engineers. That shortage will grow worse unless enough capable young men voluntarily decide to enter the field of engineering. In Soviet Russia, where everyone is told what he is expected to do, there is no shortage of engineers. Compared to the 25,000 engineers the United States is turning out every year, the Soviet Union trains 100,000 young persons for engineering. This means that every engineering graduate in this country is matched by *four* in the Soviet Union.

The problem, then, is to acquaint those young people who have the necessary special aptitudes, with the opportunities opened to them by a career in engineering. The way this book will attempt to do that is to tell the truth about engineering. Luckily, these are pleasant truths, and they describe an increasingly important and fascinating field.

The life of an engineer is anything but dull. It can be exciting and adventurous. As a young engineer you may find yourself working with a rifle at your side, prepared to fight desert bandits as you superintend the laying of oil pipelines across Arabia. You may camp on the frozen wastes of the Arctic, as a scientific prospector for uranium, or you may travel through a steaming jungle, building a railroad or a highway to bring civilization to an inaccessible area.

Or, you may be called upon to assist in man's greatest adventure—the conquest of outer space. Already small artificial satellites

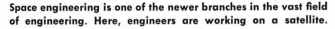

Space engineering is one of the newer branches in the vast field of engineering. Here, engineers are working on a satellite.

have been set whirling about the earth in orbits like the planets. And it is only a question of time until space platforms and rockets to the moon and other planets will be practical projects and not just dreams of fiction.

But before we get too far into the various fields of engineering, let us first examine the question: What is an engineer?

We call the man who operates the controls of a locomotive an engineer. But he is not an engineer in the real sense of the word, any more than the driver of a bus or the motorman on a street car would be an engineer in the professional sense. The locomotive engineer could not design the locomotive, or see it through the various problems of the constructional stage, or modify its design to meet different operating conditions. The man who did that for the locomotive is truly an engineer.

An engineer is not an inventor, although an engineer may invent things. For example, the man who invented the paper cup was a salesman. He thought paper cups would be a good thing, and one night in his hotel room he took scissors and paste and made the first paper cup. He later made a million dollars from the invention.

But that was only the beginning. Obviously, paper cups could not be made and sold profitably if made by hand. Besides, that would destroy one of the values of the paper cup—its sanitary qualities. The problem of designing machines that would make paper cups, and machines that would dispense them, was left to engineers. They didn't make a million dollars, but they enjoyed the challenge of solving one problem after another until the paper cup was a commercial and a practical success.

It could have been a salesman, tired of cranking his auto by hand, who invented the self-starter for automobiles. As it happened, however, the self-starter was invented by Charles F. Kettering who was an automotive engineer. Since he was an engineer, Kettering was able to follow through all the practical problems that remained to be solved before the self-starter became standard equipment on all automobiles. Kettering, as an inventor, developed many automobile patents. In every case he either had to follow through himself as the engineer in developing the idea to the manufacturing stage, or he turned the problems over to other engineers.

An engineer is different from a scientist—although an engineer may perform highly scientific work, and may even become better known as a scientist than an engineer. A scientific discovery may go through two stages of scientific research—*pure* research and *applied* research—before it reaches an engineer.

Plastics in various forms are familiar to all of us. The story of one of the earliest of plastics, Bakelite, illustrates the differences between the various kinds of scientific research and the work of the engineer—in this case the chemical engineer.

Scientists working in the field of pure research—that is, studying the nature of things without any object in view other than to increase their knowledge—had learned that small particles of matter called molecules were bound together in various ways. Some molecules are joined like the links of a chain. Others are bound compactly together; still others are a tangled jumble.

Leo Baekeland, an American chemical engineer, knew the structure of molecules as a part of his general training. In 1909 he was engaged in applied research. He was looking for an artificial resin which might improve the qualities of varnish. He knew that the natural resins obtained from trees dissolved a little too easily. He knew this was because the molecules of natural resin are bound together in long, loosely connected chains. Naturally, he was experimenting with chemicals which he hoped would form a synthetic resin with "tighter" molecules and produce a varnish which would provide a tougher film of protection for floors and furniture.

Baekeland found several combinations of chemicals which formed tougher resins and better varnish. But it was one combination which did not serve his purpose at all—a failure insofar as the object of his research was concerned—which made him famous. He discovered that carbolic acid, joined with formaldehyde by caustic soda, reacted to form a hard brown sheet. In many respects it was superior to wood.

Acid would not eat it, water and age would not rot it. And, like wood, it would not conduct electricity.

The new substance, called Bakelite, found many uses, particularly in the panels and cabinets of radio sets and electrical-system controls. But Bakelite could be made only in small sheets, and was so brittle that it was useless where strength was needed.

Bakelite was a problem child for the chemical engineer and the mechanical engineer. It is a good example of how the various fields of engineering lend a helping hand to each other. A machine was designed which would chop Bakelite into fine bits. Then the chemical engineer took over again. By adding other substances—called fillers —he could give Bakelite qualities it did not have in its original state. By mixing finely chopped canvas with the chopped Bakelite, and molding this mixture under heat and pressure, panels of greater strength could be produced. Or, if fireproof qualities were needed, these could be provided by using asbestos and mica as fillers.

The engineer is a problem solver. What do you think of that as a definition of an engineer, after having read these examples of engineers at work? The scientist is a *knowledge seeker;* the engineer is a *problem solver.* After realizing that each can be a bit of both, would you nevertheless say that the definition is a good one? Or is it too simple?

KINDS OF ENGINEERING

We have already seen a few of the different kinds of engineering. Let us take a closer look at this broad field—so complex that at first it seems bewildering and confusing. And yet we must remember that each field grew logically and slowly from its broad bases in physics, mathematics and chemistry. Each specialized field borrows from the others, and lends to them. Knowledge gained in one field cannot help but be of value in another. Many of the divisions of engineering are quite artificial. We shall see this more clearly in the chapters that follow.

Instead of listing the different branches of engineering, it might be more interesting to see how many of them enter into one project. A modern skyscraper is one kind of project which draws many kinds of engineers into its making.

Civil or *structural engineers* take the architect's plans and solve the problem of building the skyscraper to his design. Their job includes figuring and designing the foundation supports and steel girders necessary to support the building and the weight of its many floors. Structural and *mechanical engineers* supervise the excavating to bedrock for the foundation piers, and the steel and concrete work as the building rises. *Hoisting engineers* see that the building materials are raised safely and efficiently to the workers many floors above.

More engineers enter the picture as the work on the skyscraper continues. *Electrical engineers* supply the wiring system for lighting, for operating elevators and escalators, and for working pumping systems. They will cooperate with *illuminating engineers,* who see that good lighting is provided for the work that will go on in the various offices. *Heating and ventilating engineers* contribute the elaborate systems which keep the building warm in winter and cool in summer.

From the field of *chemical engineering* comes the special glass for the windows that admit healthful ultraviolet light for the building's workers. From the same field come the decorating paints, the plastic panels, the floor coverings. Mechanical engineers provide the motors and machines for operating elevators, escalators, and machinery on shipping platforms.

Traffic engineers have already entered into the planning of approaches to the building and the building's entrances, the placement and number of elevators, and the layout of the building corridors and stairways. *Sanitary engineers,* usually working for the city in which the building is located, have arranged for the building's waste matter to be carried away from its plumbing pipes into the city sewer system.

Electronics engineers are responsible for the tall TV transmitting tower atop the skyscraper, and may have been called upon to equip a floor or more of the building for radio and television broadcasting studios. On these floors where sound is important, *acoustical engineers*

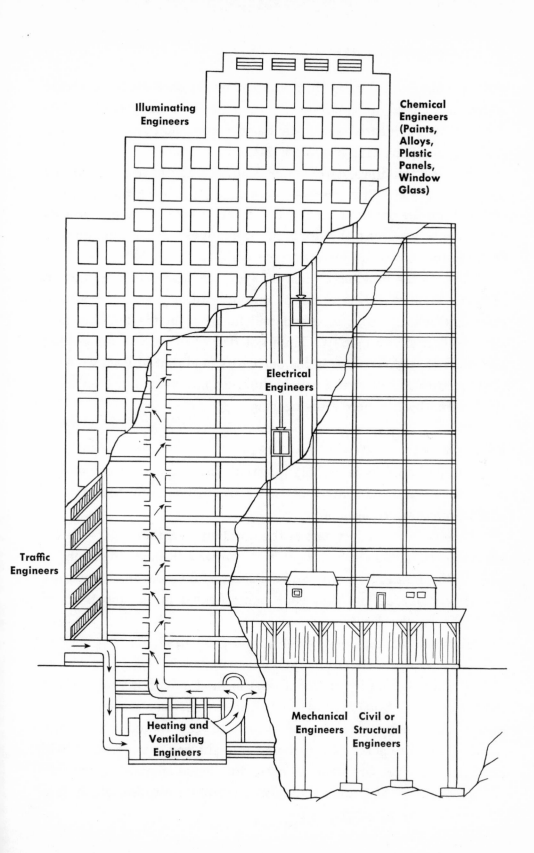

Illuminating Engineers

Chemical Engineers (Paints, Alloys, Plastic Panels, Window Glass)

Electrical Engineers

Traffic Engineers

Heating and Ventilating Engineers

Mechanical Engineers

Civil or Structural Engineers

will have been called in, as they will also be for conference or lecture rooms, or areas of the building which need to be soundproofed. *Communications engineers* have installed telephone and telegraph lines, and inter-company teletype communication systems.

On some buildings, *aeronautics engineers* will have designed and supervised the building of a helicopter landing field on the roof. For buildings on the banks of a navigable river or lake, *marine engineers* may have to supervise the dredging of channels and the building of docks so that ships can bring cargoes right to the building.

Thus, in the building of a skyscraper, we have seen the function of every kind of engineer except mining, military and agricultural engineers, who, of course, would find no place in the building of a metropolitan skyscraper. We have not described all the things that each kind of engineer does in his particular field, but at least we have a fair picture of how many widely different and yet related activities are covered by the word "engineering."

WHAT MAKES A GOOD ENGINEER?

You probably have two big questions in your mind right now— do I have the necessary aptitudes to be an engineer, and how do I go about preparing to become one?

To answer to the last part of the question: whether you're finishing up grammar school or are part of the way through high school, you can begin at once to guarantee a successful career in engineering —that is, make certain that your name figures in the top third of your class in these subjects:

Mathematics, including algebra and geometry.

Science, especially physics and chemistry.

In addition, you should be at least in the top half of your class in *English* grades. A mastery of English means an easy mastery of the many, many books you are going to have to read, in and out of classrooms, if you are going to become a top-flight engineer. English will also help you to prepare clear, accurate, intelligent engineering reports.

In addition, you must have some certain aptitudes which cannot be measured by grades. You must honestly be able to say whether or not you have these necessary qualities, or try to obtain an unbiased answer from a teacher, a relative or an older friend. (1) You must have sound habits of work and study—you *should* be able to answer this honestly yourself. (2) You must have a high degree of curiosity about things—do you wonder why fluorescent lights are made in long tubes rather than bulbs? . . why concrete highways are made in slabs rather than continuous strips? . . why radio signals are weaker in the daytime than they are at night? Are you interested in finding out the workings of the things around you? . . Have you ever, for instance, successfully improved something about the house?

There is room in engineering for all types of personalities. The quiet person with high creative abilities may do best in design work, or in chemical research. The person who likes people and who works well with them is an ideal type for civil or mechanical engineering.

Good health is especially necessary for the engineer whose work takes him into the field. But even the desk or bench engineer needs to be healthy for a job that is exacting and often calls for extra-long hours. But don't feel that you have to be a fullback husky in order to be an engineer—Charles P. Steinmetz, a wizard at electrical engineering for the General Electric Company, was a sickly, dwarflike cripple.

One important thing you should do while still in high school is to take a scientific aptitude test. Ask your counselor or any friendly teacher where you can take such a test—in many communities it is free for students. Such a test will measure your engineering aptitudes by scientific methods, and you can regard the result as fairly conclusive one way or another.

Once satisfied that engineering is your life goal, you should begin to obtain career guidance as soon as you can. A selected list of engineering institutions and schools, with addresses where you can write for bulletins and other information, will be found in the back of this book.

You may be a girl whose interest in this subject is so strong that you have ignored the title of this book and are reading it anyhow. Don't feel that the field of engineering is closed to women. It is wide open for those who show ability. There are many women in chemical engineering, and quite a few in mechanical engineering. A topflight automotive designer at one of Detroit's biggest automobile manufacturing plants is a woman. Among a recent class of more than a thousand engineering majors at the Illinois Institute of Technology, nine were girls. And women students are beginning to appear at most other engineering schools throughout the country.

You do not have to make up your mind this very moment which of the many branches of engineering you want to join. You will have plenty of time to decide that in college. Also, engineers have the opportunity of moving from one field to another as the occasion demands, and they find that their knowledge of one field actually benefits them as they work into a new one.

A company which is pioneering the development of rocket engines, makes this point clear in an appeal for engineers to join the staff. The statement said:

"It may surprise you to know you can qualify for rocket engineering without specific rocket engine experience. Engineering experience in heating and ventilating, hydraulics, pumps, turbines, combustion devices, controls and engine instrumentation are just a few of the related fields that could open your future here."

If you are one of those persons who can't decide whether he wants to be an engineer or a writer, you may be surprised to learn that you can be both! There are scores of good magazines in the various fields of engineering where a good writer or editor with an engineering degree can earn more than he would in either profession! Also, there is a demand in all these fields for technical writers who can produce booklets and reports for the engineers of a company or a group of companies engaged in a joint enterprise.

In other chapters of this book, we shall look into the various fields of engineering and trace some important developments in engineering from the earliest civilizations up to the present. Many of these milestones of engineering are still important today. But you must not assume that any of these achievements represent the best that engineers will ever do. All these developments are a mere beginning.

Those who best understand the probable steps science and engineering will take together, say that we are just on the threshold of an amazing future. The mechanical engineer of today uses only relatively efficient steam, gasoline, electric and diesel engines for power. The man who succeeds him in the future will use atomic power or energy from the sun, depending upon which of these future sources of power wins the race now in progress in research laboratories.

There are thousands of challenges to young chemical engineers—developments that promise plastics with the strength of steel; synthetic-rubber tires that will be practically indestructible; and ways to preserve food in its original state for more than a lifetime. Miracles? Yes, but you must remember that only a little more than 50 years ago the automobile and the airplane sounded like miracles, or foolish dreams of impractical men.

Those who are drawn to civil engineering will find more than a lifetime of useful work awaiting them. We as a nation have yet to solve the problems of constructing cheap and durable houses. We are going to have to rebuild our entire system of highways, clean up our rivers, learn how to control disastrous floods, and preserve the fertility of the land.

MILITARY ENGINEERING

We must not overlook the importance of our armed forces in modern engineering. There are engineers in every branch of the services, and their work is very important in peacetime and during war.

The United States Army Corps of Engineers is the largest service branch devoted to civil engineering problems. The corps has played an important part in the civilian development of the country, as well as a crucial role in war. The Corps of Engineers was organized in 1776 by George Washington, himself an engineer of many achievements. In addition to providing the engineering skills necessary to move troops over enemy territory in wartime, the Corps of Engineers has built many peacetime bridges, canals, and dams, both in the continental United States and in its possessions. The Panama Canal was completed by Army engineers. The Corps of Engineers also is responsible for the maintenance of all of the navigable rivers and inland waterways of the United States.

Engineers specializing in aeronautics, electronics, chemistry, physics and ordinary construction engineering are also found in the United States Navy, Coast Guard, Marine Corps, and Air Force. Engineers in all these services cooperate with civilian engineers from the research laboratories of private companies to experiment on the frontiers of great engineering achievements. Experiments with long-range rockets, which eventually will lead to travel in outer space as well as providing us with intercontinental missiles, are carried on independently by the Army, Navy and Air Force.

All graduates of West Point, the United States Military Academy, and of the United States Naval Academy at Annapolis, are given basic instruction in engineering. Thus, every army and navy officer in our services is acquainted at least with the basics of engineering. Of course, some of the students at these academies specialize in engineering, and spend their entire military careers on engineering projects.

While it is true that a great deal of the advanced engineering is done for the services by hired civilian engineers, the armed services must have a corps of trained engineers to coordinate and direct the work of these various civilian engineering firms and individuals.

EDWARD L. THROM

The Boy Engineer

Many of our modern tools have evolved from those used by prehistoric man.

CHAPTER ONE

PREHISTORIC MAN AS AN ENGINEER

HOW old is engineering? As a profession, not so very old—much younger than the professions of medicine and law, for example.

But in the truest sense, there have always been engineers. In the Introduction an engineer was defined as a problem solver. By that definition, men may be considered to have become engineers when they realized the limitations of the human hand. The student of anatomy correctly maintains that the hand is a marvelously engineered instrument. It is capable of more skills and more delicate responses than any tool or machine ever built by man. The same hand that can pick up a tiny and delicate object with thumb and forefinger can clench itself into a fist and deliver a forceful blow. But all of us know from our own experience that there are definite limits to the things we can do with our hands alone.

At some stage, long before there was any written history, man had to depend on his bare hands to snatch the food he needed to keep himself alive. We can only guess as to how long ago this was—but the most expert guesses suggest that it was at least 500,000 years ago. Man, at that time, was chiefly a hunter of small animals. Somehow he learned to pick up rocks and sticks and strike with them, even to throw them at his game.

Perhaps it was by accident or experiment that man discovered that stones and sticks could become useful tools when guided by his hands. He may even have learned this by watching animals, birds and insects. Nowadays, it is possible for us to observe the various creatures and thus learn their interesting habits. The burrowing wasp uses a pebble to smooth the ground after it has buried its eggs. There are

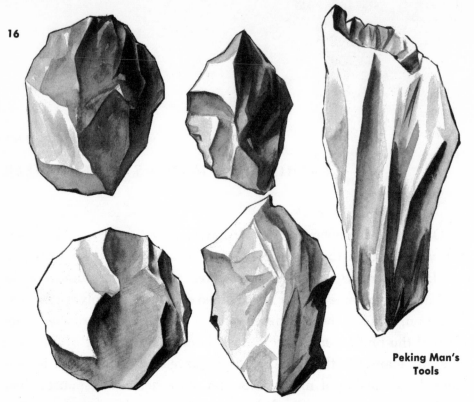

Peking Man's Tools

several species of birds which use twigs held in their beaks to pry insects from beneath the bark of trees. The southern sea otter feeds on shellfish which it picks from the floor of the sea. When the otter brings up hard-shelled varieties, it also carries a flat stone to the surface. Floating on its back on the surface, the otter then places the flat rock on its chest and smashes the shellfish against the rock. Monkeys, baboons and chimpanzees use rocks to kill hard-shelled insects, and they use sticks to knock fruit from trees.

MAN AS A TOOLMAKER

Man's use of tools began to differ from the way animals use them when he began to improve on the sticks and stones he picked up. At first this intelligence showed itself in a better selection of tools. He began to use the pronged horns of certain animals as picks and weapons. He found that tusks and jawbones could be used to scrape and cut. The jagged ends of broken sticks and animal leg bones provided him with long, pointed instruments.

One tool that man used for more than a hundred thousand years was the sharp-edged hand axe. Any conveniently sized rock with an edge sharp enough for crude cutting, chopping and scraping operations would serve his purpose. Sometimes he found stones in the beds of streams, water-worn to the needed edge or point. Others were found smashed into suitable shapes by the accident of a rock slide. Still others must have been made, accidentally at first, by man himself when he broke a stone with which he was pounding, and found sharp-edged fragments among the pieces.

Peking man, a short but sturdy ancestor of modern man, who lived in caves in northern China a hundred thousand years ago, was one of the first toolmakers. There is evidence that Peking man chipped out crude tools in his cave dwellings. We are able to put together some details concerning his toolmaking from the relics found in these caves. Using a flat stone as an anvil, Peking man smashed one stone with another stone. Then he studied the broken pieces to see if a suitable tool had resulted from the smashing. Sometimes he obtained flakes with sharp edges that could be used for cutting or scraping. Sometimes the core of unshattered rock would be left with a point which he could use to pierce holes in hides and wooden tools.

At first, Stone Age man used every kind of stone indiscriminately in his toolmaking, and the quality and shape of his tools were crude. Later, however, he learned that flint and quartz made better, sharper tools. Also, he learned to work with stone so that it would more closely take the shapes he wanted.

THE SKILLED FLINT WORKERS

It is amazing to realize that engineering principles of stress and strain can be recognized in the methods used by skilled flint workers of the Stone Age in making tools and weapons. We shall see in a moment that these primitive flint-tool makers deserve a great deal of respect for their skill.

Try this yourself. Take a small stone to the workshop, or outside to a flat stone, and smash the small stone with a hammer. You will see that the fracture of the stone does not take place in the same direc-

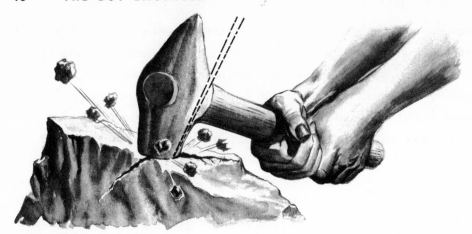

It is possible to make a piece of a rock break off in a desired direction by striking a blow at an angle of approximately 120° from the direction of fracture.

tion as the direction of the force of the blow. You will find, upon examination, that the stone is cracked in a direction downward and outward from the force of the blow.

Somehow Stone Age man learned in a general way what civil engineers know precisely today—that the direction of stone fracture resulted from a combination of the force of the blow and the angle from which the blow was struck. The flint workers found they could make a piece of rock break off in the direction they wished by striking a blow roughly at an angle of 120 degrees from the direction of fracture desired.

Knowing exactly how the stone was going to behave, the Stone Age toolmaker would find it easy to break off one side of a rock, leaving a flat side. Then he could break off the flat side in a thin slice. Using the same technique of blows directed at the proper angle, he could sharpen the edges of the stone slice.

This method had one disadvantage. At every point where a fragment of stone had been chipped away there was a shallow spot, making the edge as a whole scalloped and irregular in line. The modern engineer would call these shallow places *bulbs of percussion* as they resulted from the force of the blow necessary to chip away the flake of stone.

Yet somehow, during the course of thousands of years of toolmaking, the Stone Age engineer managed to solve this problem. Although he still used the old method of percussion pounding for the preliminary shaping of the tool, he developed a new way of fashioning edges and points. Instead of a hard rock, he used a rounded hammer of softer material—a bone, a piece of wood, or even a weather-softened rock. These blows with a soft hammer were directed at the very edge itself. This resulted in the removal of a straight, thin flake, and left none of the bulbs of percussion that had spoiled his earlier cutting edges.

Later, by still more thousands of years, the flint-tool makers learned to put even finer edges on their tools by pressure flaking. In this method the flint was not struck a blow, but tiny flakes were removed by *pressing* against the edge with a flaking tool of bone or wood.

Finally, by careful grinding against a piece of wet sandstone, the prehistoric toolmaker could put an edge on his tools as sharp as could be desired. Flint tools continued to be used long after metal tools

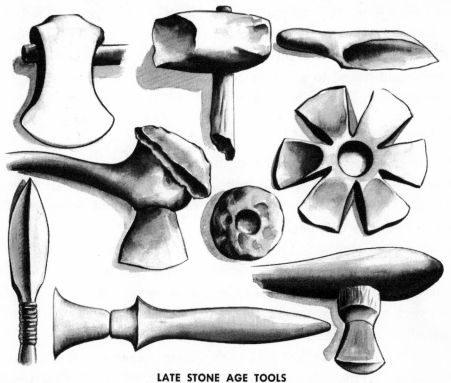

LATE STONE AGE TOOLS

were invented. This was because the toolmaker's art was producing an edge sharper than could be obtained from metal. True, the flint was more brittle, but it was easier to get than metal, and a new flint tool could easily be made when the old one broke.

In the Late Stone Age, primitive man made a wide variety of ingenious tools. With sharp flint knives he fashioned wood into bows and arrows and handles for spears, axes and digging tools. With the same flint knives he could cut pieces of bone and shell into fishhooks and crude sewing needles. With a bow, a thong and a flint drill he could bore holes in wood or make a fire, as Boy Scouts do today.

At the very end of the Stone Age men were learning to combine various materials. They drilled holes in their flint axe heads to permit the insertion of wooden handles, and shaped the handles of knives and daggers so that they would fit comfortably in the hand. They were solving problems—engineering problems—in their toolmaking. The heads of flint tools were tied into hoops of tough fiber reed with thongs of animal hide. This fastening was made tight with "glue" of resinous tree gums or with bitumen, a kind of natural asphalt. One of the finest examples ever found of this kind of work is a dagger, its blade made of jasper and flaked to a razor's edge. The handle, of smooth wood, is fastened to the blade with bitumen.

MAKE YOUR OWN STONE AGE AXE

It ought to be fun to make your own flint axe, in the same way the cave dweller did. It will look great hanging on the wall of your room. And making it will help you understand and appreciate the skills of the earliest engineers.

Start by obtaining a piece of flint or quartz from four to six inches in diameter. Perhaps you know where you can find some rocks of this type—if not, you can buy them at a hobby store. You'd better get several, for it will take a little practice to learn the cave man's technique in applying force at just the proper angle.

You can use another rock to deliver the blows if you insist—but you'll find it much easier to use the rounded head of a ball-peen ham-

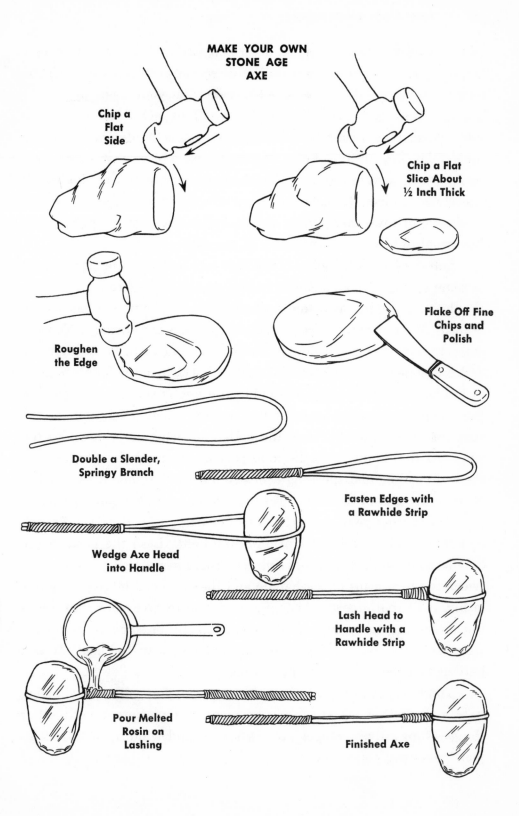

MAKE YOUR OWN STONE AGE AXE

Chip a Flat Side

Chip a Flat Slice About ½ Inch Thick

Roughen the Edge

Flake Off Fine Chips and Polish

Double a Slender, Springy Branch

Fasten Edges with a Rawhide Strip

Wedge Axe Head into Handle

Lash Head to Handle with a Rawhide Strip

Pour Melted Rosin on Lashing

Finished Axe

mer. Using the technique we described earlier—that is, striking a blow at a 120-degree angle from the direction in which you wish the rock to fracture—try to get one flat side from your piece of flint or quartz. Then try to break a slice about half an inch thick off this flat side. Then, with a smaller hammer, and using lighter blows, put a rough edge on your axe. For a finer edge, use a piece of wood or some springy tool, such as a putty knife, to apply light pressure, flaking off fine chips. Finish the edge by sharpening both sides on a piece of sandstone or knife-sharpening stone. Polish the flint or quartz with steel wool to bring out the beauty of the stone.

For the handle of your Stone Age axe, select a slender branch of some springy wood, such as willow or elm. The branch could be about as big around as a thick pencil. Cut off about two feet of the branch. Make sure the part you choose is green and springy. You are going to have to bend it double, so that the ends can be brought together and tied. The ends are fastened with a strip of rawhide, about 18 inches long. You can get the rawhide at a hobby store. Lay a strip of this rawhide along the ends of the branch, starting one end of the strip about 8 inches up from the ends and bringing it down to the ends. At that point wrap the long part of the rawhide strip around the ends, coiling and spiraling it neatly until within about two inches of the other end of the strip. Tie the two ends neatly and tightly.

Now wedge your axe head into the curved bend of the branch handle, shifting it until it is firm and straight. Lash the head to the handle with another strip of rawhide. Force some of the lashing between the bent arms of the handle and the axe head to give a tighter lashing. To reinforce the fastening and also to give your flint axe a touch of authenticity, melt a little piece of rosin or some blobs of gum from a cherry tree and pour this around the head lashings. It will harden as it cools and keep the lashing tight.

You'll be proud of your Stone Age axe and you will enjoy showing it to your friends. You may even want to experiment with other things—flint knives, daggers, arrowheads—and wind up with a complete cave-man collection.

THE FIRST MINING ENGINEERS

Mining is one of the oldest of engineering activities. Before the Stone Age was over, man was digging deep into the ground in search of better grades of flint than he could find on the surface. The earliest of these mines were simple pit shafts, dug through several layers

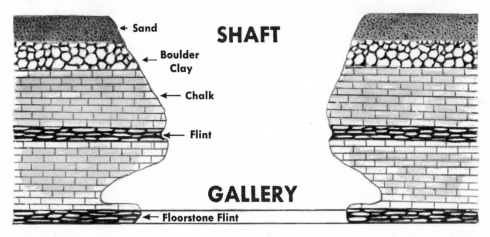

The earliest mines that man ever dug were simple pit shafts dug down through several layers of earth. This was the humble beginning of mining engineering.

of poor flint until the good, hard floorstone flint was struck. Even though they are only holes in the ground, ranging from 10 to 15 feet deep, these mines represented much hard labor. For the only tools used were the sharpened leg bones of oxen or other animals, or picks made from animal horns.

Soon these prehistoric miners learned to follow a vein of flint sideward from the shaft by which they had reached it. Extending these galleries into the vein brought them more good flint. But it brought them a problem that mining engineers of today must still take into account. This was the fact that the roofs of these galleries were apt to collapse without warning. The skeleton of one Stone Age miner found in an ancient gallery in Belgium is a tragic example of what happened. The skeleton, on hands and knees and with an antler pick nearby, was crushed through back and neck by the fall of the gallery roof. Later Stone Age men learned, under the spur of such ac-

When man learned to follow the veins in the mines he dug, he had to learn how to keep the roof of the mine from collapsing. He learned to leave stone pillars or timber poles to support the roof of the mine.

cidents, to leave pillars of stone to hold up the roof, or to support it with timber poles.

It is not known whether mining for flint led directly to the mining of metals. Perhaps the first men to find metal saw it in the beds of streams or the exposed sides of rocks on the surface. This metal was in a pure state, and there was very little of it. Gold, silver and copper were the metals commonly found, and they were mostly used for ornaments and small objects like piercing needles and fishhooks. Later on, as men began to find larger quantities of pure metal, perhaps in mines originally dug for flint, they began to make tools and weapons. They found that metal became harder when it was pounded into shape. On the other hand, melted metal could be poured into a mold and cooled to a particular shape. These first metal tools and weapons were very soft, according to our standards. For thousands of years, the old flint tools served man's needs much better.

Here and there, however, toolmakers continued to experiment with native copper nuggets and sheets. Somehow they found that the brittleness of copper could be overcome to some extent by heating it and cooling it slowly, then cold-working it into shape. This heating and slow cooling is called *annealing*.

The supply of fairly pure copper was limited. It was necessary to mine for the purple, green and black rocks which men had learned would show the bright gleam of copper when they scratched it. And then, to get the copper separated from its ore, these men began that branch of engineering called *metallurgy*. They developed *smelting*, which takes advantage of the fact that under high heat, the metals and the impurities in raw ore melt at different stages of the process.

If you can obtain some copper ore, the use of an outdoor barbecue oven and a fireplace bellows, you can smelt copper the way Neolithic man did. You might find it fun to try, and perhaps beat out a bracelet or a good-luck charm from the crudely refined metal. Here is what these first metallurgists did:

In a small furnace, they alternated layers of charcoal and copper ore. As the charcoal burned and melted the ore, the copper went to the bottom of the mass in a spongy layer, while the impurities in the ore united with the charcoal cinders in a mass of slag on top. Prying the copper mass away from the slag, the early metal smelter put it through another smelting process, this time blowing air into the mass with a long blowpipe or a bellows made from an animal's hide. The blast of air caused *oxidation* of the impurities in the ore—that is, they united with the oxygen in the blast of air. This time the copper would contain relatively few impurities. It could then be pounded hard (cold-worked), annealed, and cold-worked again.

THE BRONZE AND IRON AGES

The early metalworkers discovered that the brightest and purest copper made soft metal, which could be hardened by hammering. But the hardening made the metal brittle. Weapons and tools made of this bright copper were too apt to break. But darker copper, from ores which they recognized contained dark-silver metals, made tools which were hard and tensile (they bent a little without breaking). Thus the first *alloy* (the combining of two or more metals) was an accident. The better tools and weapons were being made from bronze, an alloy made of copper combined with tin or zinc. You can easily tell the difference between a soft copper wire (almost pure copper) and a penny (an alloy of copper, tin and zinc).

When the metalworkers discovered that the better weapons and tools were made from such ores as contained tin and zinc as well as copper, they had made an important discovery. Ores with the proper combinations were hard to find. But it was simple enough to find copper and tin ores separately, then combine them in the smelting.

The ability to smelt a harder metal such as bronze led to the creation of a number of new tools for working with wood. These new tools included chisels, drills, files and even crude saws.

A few iron tools and ornaments have been found which are believed to date back even before the Bronze Age. But by their high content of nickel, scientists suspect that this iron was from meteorites. You probably know how particles of matter blaze through the universe, developing high heat from friction when they strike the earth's atmosphere. So high is this heat that the meteorite is smelted into an alloy of iron and nickel before it reaches the earth. Men of the Stone Age must have found these meteorite fragments and fashioned them into tools before they knew how to smelt any metal.

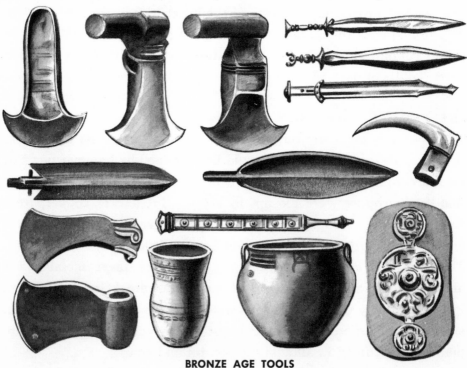

BRONZE AGE TOOLS

Bronze Age smelters must have experimented with iron ores. But they probably saw little to encourage them in the spongy gray mass that results from the simple smelting of iron. Later they learned to beat this mass, or "bloom," into wrought iron. But this was brittle and would not take a good edge—it was certainly no improvement over bronze.

A true Iron Age did not begin until about 1200 B.C., relatively late in the long history of the world. It was the discovery of hardening by *tempering*—the heating and quick quenching of iron in water—that led to tools and weapons of iron that were stronger than bronze.

PREHISTORIC CIVIL ENGINEERING

It must be understood that while man was developing the tools we have been talking about, his life was changing in many ways. Instead of wandering about in search of wild grains and game, man now began to settle in one place. Digging tools enabled him to plant crops more easily. The making of flint and bronze tools and weapons made it necessary that at least part of the group stay at home to make the arrowheads for the hunters. Other men became full-time specialists in the growing of crops. Thus, at a time before history was written, the first villages were formed.

These first villages rose, quite naturally, along the banks and mouths of rivers where the climate was good and the soil rich enough for crude farming. One such region was the valley of the Nile River in Egypt. We shall find ourselves talking about this region a great deal as we trace the history of engineering. We must remember, at the same time, that there were other regions like this—in India, in Central America, in Peru, and in Europe—where villages were formed and man's engineering skills grew because of this closer association.

The first efforts at home building, where natural caves could not be found, were simply burrows dug into the ground and roofed with logs laid side by side and covered with earth. Later there were crude efforts at pole structures, covered tentlike with skins. In Egypt, there are evidences of prehistoric houses which had a framework of branches around which were set walls of mud. There were even post-holes and evidences of a framed doorway.

Much later in the long history of Egypt, builders began to use planks to cover their house frames, and still later to build with crude bricks of sun-dried mud.

In Europe, during the Stone and Bronze Ages, a group of men known as the Lake Dwellers built frame houses much as we do small houses today. They had slanting (pitched) roofs to shed water, and the larger ones had inner pillars to support the weight of the roof. By the time of the Iron Age, the houses of the Lake Dwellers were very large. A house held several families, each with its own cooking hearth. Some of these frame-house villages were quite elaborate, with log roads leading from one house to another, and high walls surrounding the village.

In all kinds of ways, then, prehistoric man was learning to master his environment. With tools he dug up the ground for his crops, and cut down the harvest. In dry seasons he learned to cut canals leading from a river to his fields. He learned to bridge streams, at first with trees and rocks in imitation of the bridges made by accidents of nature. With boats, which were hollowed-out logs or reed baskets covered with animal skins, he could travel over the water. He learned to make sledges by which he could haul heavy loads over the ground. Then he used logs as rollers under the sledges, and then he made a wonderful discovery—he learned to make wheels.

Thus, as man entered the Bronze Age, he was becoming quite an engineer—quite a solver of problems. More and more he was using aids which employed principles of physics for which he had no name—aids which we know today as the *simple machines*.

The mechanical engineer works with many kinds of machinery. No matter how complicated this machinery is, it will be found to be, when taken part by part, a combination of the basic machines which man has been using for thousands of years.

Sometimes mechanical engineers speak of the six simple machines, calling these the *lever*, the *wheel and axle*, the *pulley*, the *inclined plane*, the *wedge* and the *screw*. Others say there are only two basic machines. They call these the lever and the inclined plane, arguing that the wheel and axle and the pulley are forms of the lever. while the wedge and the screw are forms of the inclined plane.

Let us examine the lever, one of the earliest machines man ever used. Suppose you wanted to move a rock that was heavier than you could lift, or pull a tree stump out of the ground. You could do it if you put one end of a long bar under the rock or stump, passed the bar over another rock or stump, and pushed down on the other end of the bar. As you push down, a strange thing happens—that is, you will find it strange when you begin to think about it. You are pushing down on the bar, and that part of the bar which is between you and the rock on which the bar is resting is moving downward. But that part of the bar which is between this rock and under the rock you are trying to lift is moving upward! As you push down on one end of the lever, the other end moves up and lifts the rock. This is because the rock that is between you and the load to be lifted serves as a *fulcrum*, resisting the downward movement of the bar and turning it into an upward movement at the other end. This is one of the important things that machines do—they change the direction of a force.

You will notice another important thing—the closer the fulcrum rock is to the rock which is to be lifted, the easier it is to lift the load; that is, the less pressure you have to use in pushing downward on the end of the bar. If you moved the rock closer to you and farther away from the load to be lifted, you would find it much harder to push down on the lever and lift the rock.

Let us suppose that you could, by exerting all your strength, just lift the rock with your hands, using all your arm, back and leg muscles.

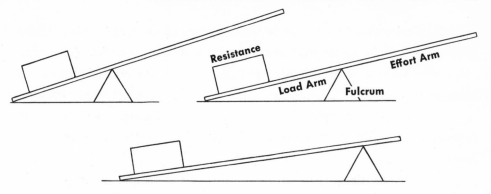

The closer the fulcrum is to the load, the easier it is to lift the load.

If the fulcrum rock were exactly halfway between you at one end of the lever bar and the rock to be lifted, you could just barely lift the rock by pushing down on your end of the bar, again using all your strength. The lever then would be of no particular advantage. If you moved the fulcrum rock still closer to you, you would not be able to lift the rock with the lever at all.

The length of the lever is also important. The longer it is, the easier you will be able to move the load. There are practical limits to this, however. In a simple situation like lifting the rock, for example, the lever could be no longer than you could reach over your head and still apply downward pressure on the bar. The upward pressure on the other end would be very great, however, and you could lift large loads with such a long bar. The mechanical advantage (MA) of a lever is a ratio between the length of the effort arm and the length of the resistance arm. The formula is:

$$MA = \frac{E}{R}$$

Thus, if the effort arm (E) of a lever was 8 feet and the resistance arm was 2 feet, the MA of the lever would be 4.

$$MA = \frac{8}{2} = 4$$

You could lift the earth—if you had a lever tens of millions of miles long. You could slip one end over Venus or Mars to serve as a fulcrum, and push on the other end of your lever from a space ship!

But we don't have to get that wild in fancy to find examples of levers. This simple machine is used by all of us every day. Every pressed-on can or jar lid that bears the instruction, "To Open, Pry Up," calls for use of a lever. Your opener, slipped under the rim of the lid, uses the side of the jar or the edge of the can as a fulcrum. Imagine the superhuman strength it would take to open such a lid with your fingers alone! But through the leverage gained with the opener, it is easily done.

A hammer driving a nail is not a lever. That is because the direction of motion of the energy applied is not changed. The mass and momentum of the hammer head, swung down, drives the nail down. But a hammer is a lever when it is used to pry up a nail. Here the energy is applied downward on the handle, while the claw end of the hammer, using the board into which the nail is driven as a fulcrum, pulls the nail up and out.

Remember in thinking about the lever that the fulcrum does not have to be between the load and the effort. The wheelbarrow is an example of a lever in which the fulcrum, the wheel, is at one end, while the load is in the middle.

The wheel and axle is a simple machine which, as we said before, may be considered as a separate machine or as simply another form of the lever. Devices like this are found over old-fashioned wells where the water is drawn up in a bucket by means of a rope which winds around an axle as the handle of a wheel is turned. The hand windlass by which the anchor is drawn up on small boats is another example of the wheel and axle. The axle serves as the fulcrum, while

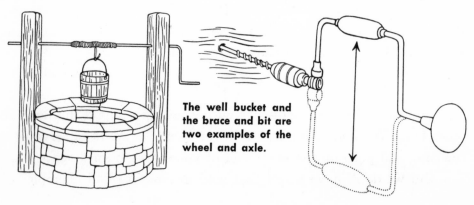

The well bucket and the brace and bit are two examples of the wheel and axle.

the handle, turning about the wheel at a distance from the axle, exerts the leverage power.

There need not actually be a wheel in order for a tool or machine to use the wheel-and-axle principle. All that is required is that the turning handle move in a circle about the axle. The device you use to tighten up the playground tennis net, and the crank the grocer uses to raise his awnings, are examples of the wheel and axle in action. Another common example is the brace and bit, that queerly-shaped hand tool used to bore holes in wood.

The pulley is another form of the wheel and axle. If you hang a single pulley from an overhead support, pass a rope over the pulley and tie one end of the rope to a load, there will be no mechanical advantage. True, it may be a little easier to lift the load by pulling down on the end of the rope. But that is only because you are better able in this position to use all the power of your muscles and the weight of your body in applying effort. A true mechanical advantage is not gained until you use two pulleys, one attached to a support and the other attached to the load. One end of the rope is attached to the axle of the suspended pulley. The rope then runs down to and around the other pulley, which is attached to the load, and the rope then goes back up and over the wheel of the suspended pulley. When you pull on the free end of the rope, the effort required will be one-half the load. This kind of pulley arrangement is said to have a mechanical advantage of two.

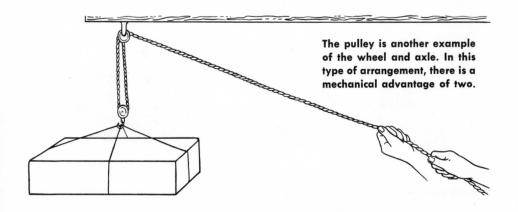

The pulley is another example of the wheel and axle. In this type of arrangement, there is a mechanical advantage of two.

In the pulley system we were talking about, the mechanical advantage was two. Thus, if the weight being lifted weighed 50 pounds, we would know that 25 pounds of effort would be required to lift it.

The more pulleys you can arrange to share the burden of the load, the easier it will be to lift the load. Thus hoisting engineers work up complicated block-and-tackle arrangements for use in lifting such heavy loads as locomotives, railroad cars, wrecked trailer trucks, huge printing presses and similar heavy lifting jobs. All these are simply pulley systems.

The inclined plane is such a simple device that you may not think it deserves to be called a machine. But it is a valuable simple machine, and you will find its principle in use in many kinds of complicated machinery, as we shall see later.

A good way to demonstrate to yourself the principle of the inclined plane can be tried the next time you are riding your bicycle. Put the front wheel of your bicycle against the curb, at right angles to it. Then, using the pedals from a standing start, try to ride up over the curb. You probably won't be able to do it. Next, try the same kind of standing start, but from the bottom of the slope that runs from the edge of the street up into a driveway. Quite easy, isn't it? That's because the upslope of the driveway is an inclined plane.

Notice how men loading heavy furniture or machinery into a truck make use of an inclined plane. Instead of trying to lift the heavy load up from the street into the truck bed, they slant a long plank

By using an inclined plane, it is easy to lift heavy objects from one level up to a higher level.

from the truck to the ground. They find it easy to slide the load up the plank and into the truck. Using a 10-foot plank to reach a truck bed two feet high, a 500-pound load could be lifted in this way with no more effort than it would require to lift a 100-pound load directly into the truck.

It was with the inclined plane that the Egyptians must have built their mighty pyramids nearly 5,000 years ago. There was, as far as we know, no hoisting machinery in those days. Nevertheless, the Egyptians managed to raise the pyramids almost as high as a modern skyscraper. And they built them with as many as 2,300,000 blocks, each weighing 2½ tons! Modern engineers reason that the blocks came from quarries on the banks of the muddy Nile River. In spring, when the river flooded its banks, the Egyptians would float the blocks on rafts to the site of a pyramid. As each tier of the pyramid was laid, a spiraling ramp made of stones and mud from the slimy Nile rose around the pyramid. Up this ramp, or inclined plane, the workers would laboriously drag the stone blocks. Perhaps they used logs as rollers under the stones. But this we do not know. The mud would become sunbaked and hard in the desert heat, but flushing water over the top of the ramp would have made it slick and reduced the friction as the blocks were dragged up. When the pyramid was completed, the ramp was simply knocked away into clods of dirt and dust, soon to be swallowed up by the shifting desert sands.

Notice that the inclined plane qualifies as a simple machine because it *changes the direction* of an effort. When you walk along an inclined plane, such as one leading from one level to another in a split-level home, your motion is forward rather than up. In mounting a staircase, however, each step is an upward movement as well as a forward step.

The wedge is another example of the inclined plane. Or, perhaps we ought to think of the wedge as two inclined planes, back to back. Here the inclined planes are in motion. For instance, take the wedge with which lumbermen split logs. Here the wedge moves into a crack in the log, driven by blows from a sledge hammer. As the wedge moves toward the heart of the log, the log splits away at right angles to the direction of the wedge.

The thinner the edge of a wedge is — that is, the more acute its angle—the greater its mechanical advantage will be, which means that less force will be required to do a given amount of work.

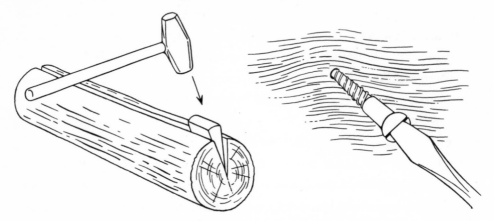

The wedge and the screw are two examples of the inclined plane.

The screw is a form of the inclined plane wrapped around a pedestal. In a wood screw, with the tapering pedestal, the inclined plane is combined with the wedge to allow the screw to force its way into wood with the relatively small effort supplied by a screwdriver.

The jackscrew is a highly efficient machine which combines the usefulness of the screw with that of the lever. By exerting an effort of one pound on the lever of a jackscrew, one man can lift 1,500 pounds!

Gears are important simple machines to change the direction of motion. Gears are wheels with teeth so spaced that the teeth will fit into the spaces of another gear and the spaces of the first gear will accept the teeth of the second gear. Naturally, as one gear turns, the other gear will turn with it, but in the opposite direction.

But changing the direction of motion is not the most important thing gears do. Rather more important is the fact that they can change the speed of the motion. Two gears of equal size will turn with equal speed. But a large gear, whose teeth take a long time to make the turn around the axle, will make a small gear spin rapidly

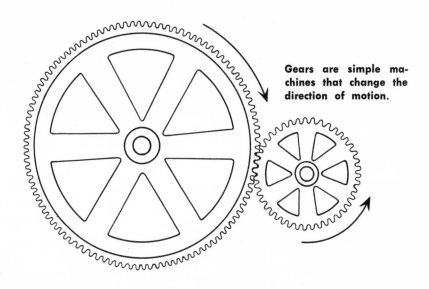

Gears are simple machines that change the direction of motion.

in the opposite direction. Very complicated gearing systems are set up by mechanical engineers to supply the correct transmission of power and direction of motion to very intricate machines.

Your bicycle combines the gear, the pulley, and the wheel and axle. Can you find them?

Shafts and yokes are other examples of machines which change the direction of motion. Suppose a piston engine, whether steam, gasoline or diesel, is imparting a back-and-forth motion to a drive shaft. Suppose you want to change this back-and-forth, or linear motion, to a circular, or rotary motion. One way to do this would be to connect a drive shaft to a wheel with an eccentric arm. An eccentric arm is a short shaft that has one end fastened to the axis of the wheel. This end is concentric. It is to the other end, the eccentric arm, that you attach the drive shaft of your engine. You also need a linking arm between the drive shaft and the concentric arm which will follow the wheel about in a rotary motion as the drive shaft goes back and forth in its linear motion. This gets rather complicated in a word description, but the pictures on page 38 will explain what happens.

A wheel, drive pin and slotted yoke is another mechanical means of changing motion. Suppose that this time you had a circular motion which you wanted to change into a linear motion. This could be done

Piston and Crank—Circular Motion

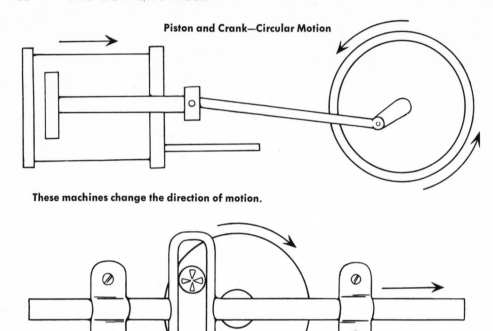

These machines change the direction of motion.

Shaft and Yoke—Linear Motion

by fitting a revolving wheel with an eccentric stub, called a drive pin, which fits into a slotted yoke. The drive pin follows the circular motion of the wheel, but at every point in the circular movement the pin exerts force against the side of the slotted yoke, making the yoke and the rod it is attached to go back and forth.

Why all this fuss about changing the direction of motion, you may ask? Why don't engineers just design their machines to develop the proper motion in the first place? Well, there are many reasons why the end results of a machine cannot be achieved in the first step. Take the family automobile, for instance. An automobile engine operates most efficiently when its cylinders and pistons work up and down. But, of course, an up-and-down motion wouldn't be of much use in moving an automobile over the streets. So the up-and-down motion of the pistons is changed into a rotary motion, which still is not of much use, for the direction is sidewise. But by means of gears, this motion is changed to a circular one forward, and, of course, can also be reversed to make the car back up. Gears also are used to make the car operate at various levels of efficiency at different speeds.

Engineers make use of these simple machines we have discussed to build many complex and wonderful devices. Let us analyze one of them—the power shovel—which takes the place of thousands of pick-and-shovel men in construction work. Let us see how many of our simple machines we can find at work in one of these mighty earth-diggers.

First of all, the controls operated by the man in the power shovel cab are levers, which easily move and mesh gears he would find impossible to engage by hand. The tractor treads on which the power shovel moves so easily over rough, sloping ground are really inclined planes in motion. Over the fixed arm of the power shovel runs a set of cables in a complicated pulley system which lowers, raises and empties the huge bucket. A movable arm acts as a lever when the bucket digs into a pile of dirt or rocks. And the jaws of the bucket are wedged so they can pry out stubborn loads. The cab of the power shovel is raised and lowered by a jackscrew. We have, therefore, found most of our simple machines in operation, without even getting into the complex inner machinery of a power shovel!

The power shovel is a compound machine—which simply means that it is a machine made up of combinations of the simple machines we have been discussing. This is the job of the engineer, to find machines which will do a particular job with a high degree of efficiency.

Modern engineers are pretty good at this. As one example of how good they are, take note of the biggest gates in the world, those which open and close the locks of the Panama Canal. Some of these gates, all made of steel, are 7 feet thick, 65 feet wide and 82 feet high. The steel in all these gates would weigh about as much as all the steel in the Empire State Building. Yet a 25-horsepower electric motor swings a pair of them open or shut in 2 minutes! This is accomplished, of course, by mounting the gates in precise balance, and operating them by an intricate system of weights, levers and gears. The motor that supplies the initial energy is not a great deal more powerful than the electric motor that runs your family's washing machine, and only about 100 times the horsepower of the motor whirling the average electric fan!

SOME EXPERIMENTS YOU CAN PERFORM

To prove to yourself (and that's the only way to really learn) the mechanical advantage of a lever, make one yourself, and use an instrument to measure its efficiency. The lever can be any sturdy length of wood or metal bar that can be marked into divisions with chalk or crayon. Find the center of the lever and mark that. Then find the center of each half, and divide each of these equally, until your lever is marked with eight equal divisions. You will need a fulcrum— a rock or a block of wood or a sturdy box. Also you will need a weight, or load—anything handy weighing at least several pounds. Finally, you will need a small spring scale that you can borrow, or pick up at a hardware or variety store for a small price.

First, weigh your weight, or load, with the spring scale. Let us say that the weight is a bag of sand which weighs five pounds when hung from the spring scale. Now attach the weight to one end of the lever, and the spring scale to the other end. Place the lever over the fulcrum at the line which marks the center of the lever. Now pull down on the spring scale so that it tips the lever, lifts the weight and at the same time gives you a reading of the weight. If your lever is exactly centered, the scale will read at 5 pounds. This means that it took five pounds of effort to lift five pounds of weight. There is no mechanical advantage here. All your lever accomplished was to change the direction of the motion.

Now move the lever over so that the fulcrum is halfway between the weight and the center mark, leaving the scale on the longer side of the lever. Move the lever to lift the weight, and you will find that the scale reveals that it takes only 2½ pounds of effort to lift the 5-pound weight! This is a mechanical advantage of 2 to 1. Another way of thinking about it is that your lever has made the 5-pound

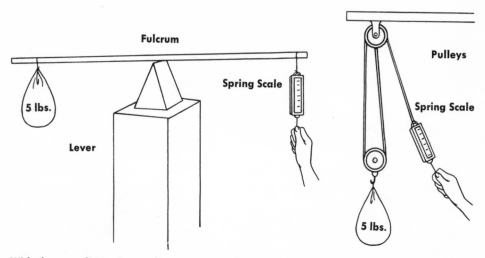

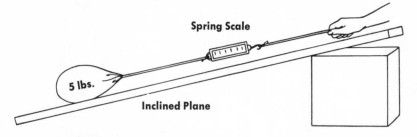

With the use of a spring scale, you can experiment
with the efficiency of these three simple machines.

bag weigh only 2½ pounds.

To continue the experiment, try the fulcrum at the other points
marked along your lever. Write down the scale readings, and figure
out the mechanical advantage (if any) of each mark.

Buy or borrow a couple of small pulleys, and rig them up with
a strong cord as shown in the drawing. Now try lifting your 5-pound
bag of sand, reading the scale to find the mechanical advantage your
system of pulleys has achieved.

Experiment with an inclined plane by taking a fairly long board
and propping one end up at various heights. Reading the scale as
you pull the 5-pound bag of sand slowly up these various degrees
of angles, note how the effort must be increased as the angle of the
plane becomes greater. Nevertheless, it is always less than the effort
(5 pounds) required to lift the bag straight up.

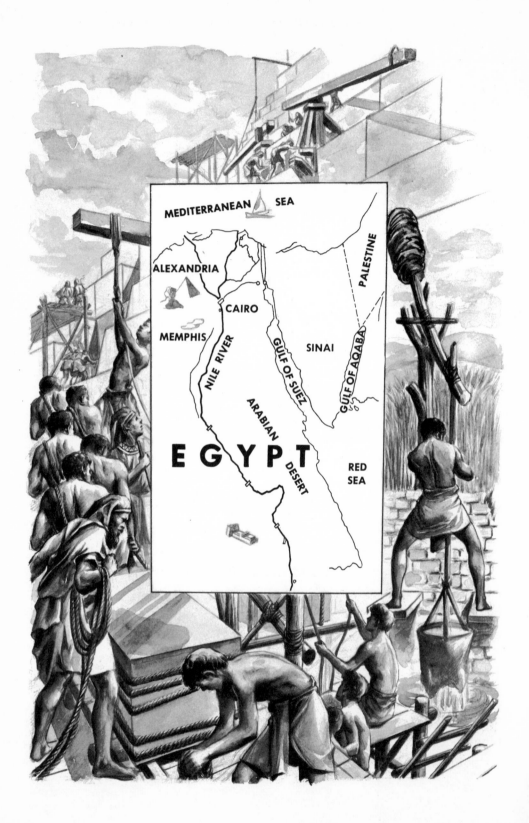

MEDITERRANEAN SEA

ALEXANDRIA

PALESTINE

CAIRO

MEMPHIS

NILE RIVER

GULF OF SUEZ

SINAI

GULF OF AQABA

ARABIAN DESERT

EGYPT

RED SEA

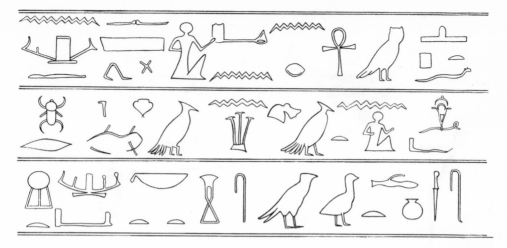

The first writing man ever did was picture writing. This enabled him to express his ideas, and to record important events in his life.

CHAPTER TWO

THE ANCIENT EGYPTIANS

WE do not know very much about the beginnings of speech, writing, or the ability of early man to use numbers. Anthropologists—those who study man in all his developments—believe that Stone Age man developed his language at about the same time he was learning to make tools. It is probable that he used a mixture of words and gestures to communicate with others in his group.

The first writing, of course, was picture writing. It did a fairly good job of expressing ideas and recording events. On the wall of a cave in Europe is a drawing made more than 20,000 years ago. It tells us, today, what the artist wished to tell when he drew it on the cave wall in crude-earth colors with a brush made from the end of a reed. The drawing shows a bison, its side pierced by a spear, driving its horns into the hunter who threw the spear. The message the artist wished to reach all hunters: *Be sure you hit your game in a vital spot!*

How speech and writing developed is important to the story of engineering because they indirectly led to a system of numbers, then to simple measurements, and finally to a system of mathematics. These we know are highly important to engineering.

We have found many drawings that decorated the walls of Stone Age caves.

Anthropologists believe that the first men had a very limited knowledge of numbers. They probably had nothing more than a sense of "one-ness," "two-ness," and "three-ness"—that is, they were able to distinguish between one thing, two of them, and sometimes three. Any number of things over three probably became "many." There are animals believed to be this clever in distinguishing numbers of things.

Language and picture writing undoubtedly helped man to grasp the idea of larger numbers. But there is evidence that he was also helped by a study of his fingers and toes—since all the early ways of expressing numbers gave special emphasis to 5 and 10.

Scientists and high-school students alike use some of these primitive methods of counting even today—because they are so convenient. All of us have had occasion to keep track of a count of things by making, up to four marks like this: | | | |.   At five, we set the group aside by marking across the four like this: ‖‖. As we count, we make a series of these symbols for five. When the count is ended, it is a simple matter to count by fives and add the extra strokes to the total. Such a total can be reached very quickly, as ‖‖ ‖‖ ‖‖ | | | is readily seen to total 18. Such a system is efficient when you have to keep a count of things while being interrupted.

Whether with notches on a stick or strokes made on wet clay or crude paper, the ancient civilizations recorded numbers in much the same way.

The Egyptians made strokes up to |||| .   Then at five they made three strokes and began a new row, like this: |||
||

while six was written thusly: ||| and seven: ||||
||| |||

Eight was written |||| while nine was ||| At ten the symbol
|||| |||
              |||

changed from a simple stroke to ∩ , something like an upside-down "U." A mark like a "C" represented 100, while 1,000 had a fancy drawing like this: ⚘. This is not too different from the Roman numerals with which we are all familiar: I, II, III and IV standing for 1, 2, 3, 4, and V, VI, VII, VIII, representing 5, 6, 7, 8, and IX and X standing for 9 and 10.

With a numbering system, it was a simple step for man to develop a system of measurements. Up to this point, his buildings had been rather crude and irregular in shape. The length, width and height of his houses depended more on the material he had at hand than on any planned measurements.

Another important change made it necessary to have measurements. Man was now building for other men, rather than building only for himself. When a man built his own hut, he could say to himself: "It will be as long as twelve of *my* steps and as as wide as eight of *my* steps. The roof will be higher than my head by the breadth of *my* hand." But when groups of men were building for the temple priests or the village rulers, their paces and their hand-breadths would vary, and would be useless as measurements.

Nevertheless, the first measurements were based on the proportions of a man's body. Early workmen often measured by putting their forearms along a length of material and marking off the distance from the elbow to the end of the middle finger. The Egyptian royal

COMPARISON OF MEASUREMENTS   (To Scale)

cubit was obtained in this way by measuring the forearm of their king. This distance was then marked off on a number of rods and used as a standard of measurement in all Egyptian buildings. The royal cubit measured about 20½ inches. The cubit was divided into seven "palms," based on the width of four fingers of a man's hand. Each palm was a little less than 3 inches. Each palm was divided into four digits, or the width of a man's finger, this being about ¾ of an inch by our standards of measurement.

Our own foot measurement stems from early systems of measurement based on the length of a man's foot. These early "feet" were remarkably close to our own 12-inch foot. The ancient Greek foot and those of medieval England and Germany were only a little longer than 12 inches (12.44, 12.47 and 12.36 inches). The foot of the ancient Roman measurements was a little less than our foot, being 11.66 inches.

We have told you something of these great engineering achievements—the Pyramids. They seem even greater when considered with the fact that the Egyptian builders had no wheels or any machinery beyond the simple machines.

One thing the Egyptians did know was how to make a square corner. They made the corners of their buildings and temples and pyramids square in the same way that a house builder does today. Try to be around the next time builders start laying the foundation of a new house in your neighborhood. You will see many builders of small houses staking out a corner in the same way as did the Egyptians. They make a triangle of stakes driven into the ground and connected by a cord, or perhaps with stakes and light pieces of lumber connecting the stakes in a triangular form.

But this is not just any triangle. Always there will be a relationship of lengths between stakes which results in a right angle being formed opposite the longest side. Experiment in making triangles on a sheet of paper with pencil and ruler. One combination that will give you a right angle is a triangle with sides 3 inches, 4 inches and 5 inches long. This is an easy one to remember—3, 4, 5—and by joining three stakes together in this relationship using feet instead of inches, you can form a right angle, with which to start the first corner of a house, a garage, or any other building.

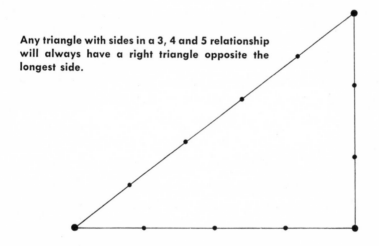

Any triangle with sides in a 3, 4 and 5 relationship will always have a right triangle opposite the longest side.

The Egyptians laid so much tile that they must have discovered early in their studies how to find the area of a square or an oblong. They could not have laid many squares or rectangles of tile before discovering that the total number of tiles in such an area was always the number of tiles along the length of one side times the number of tiles along the width of one side.

From finding the area of a rectangle, it was only another step to finding the area of a right triangle (multiplying its base, or length,

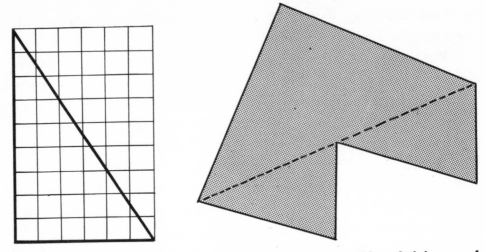

By using the rule for finding the area of a right triangle, it is possible to find the area of many shapes.

by its height or width, and dividing by 2). The surveyors of the fields along the fertile Nile found this a handy way to survey and find the size of irregularly shaped plots of land. No matter how irregular an area may be, it can be divided into a number of right triangles so long as the area itself is made up of straight sides.

Try this on the irregular area outlined and shaded in gray on this page. See if you can divide it with a pencil and ruler into a number of right triangles. Then, using the formula in the paragraph above, obtain the area of each triangle, and then, by adding the totals, the area of the outlined shape.

The circle was no mystery to the Egyptian scribes. One of them put this rule on papyrus nearly 4,000 years ago: *The area of a circle is very nearly three and one-seventh times as great as the area of a square drawn on its radius.* As we know, the radius of a circle is the distance of a straight line drawn from the center of the circle to any point on the edge, or circumference. If you take a compass and spread the center point and pencil arm 2 inches apart on a ruler, you can draw a circle with a 2-inch radius. Making the radius one side of a square, as in the illustration, you would mark off an area of 4 square inches. Now let us apply the ancient Egyptian formula: $3\frac{1}{7} \times 4 = 12\frac{4}{7}$ square inches.

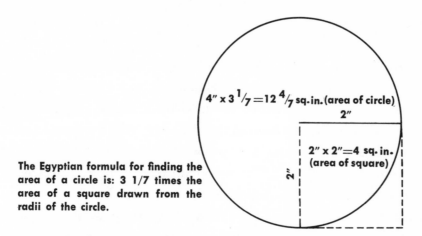

$4'' \times 3\frac{1}{7} = 12\frac{4}{7}$ sq.-in. (area of circle)

2''

$2'' \times 2'' = 4$ sq.- in. (area of square)

2''

The Egyptian formula for finding the area of a circle is: 3 1/7 times the area of a square drawn from the radii of the circle.

How accurate was the Egyptian formula by modern methods of computation? Let us see. We now know that there is a definite, if not quite precise, relationship between the area of a circle and its radius. We call this relationship *pi*, and say that the area of a circle is 3.142 times the square of the radius. The square of the radius of our circle is 4. *Pi*, or 3.142 $\times$ 4=12.568 square inches. The Egyptians were pretty close!

THE EGYPTIANS AS ENGINEERS

How did the Egyptians put their knowledge of mathematics and the simple machines to use? They managed to accomplish a great deal with comparatively little. We have discussed some of their building methods. Now let us look at some of their other endeavors from an engineering standpoint.

Agriculture and irrigation: The farming methods of the ancient Egyptians were very crude. Ground was broken by wooden plows, roped at first to men, and later to oxen. The grain was cut with wooden sickles, into which flint edges were set.

In bringing water to their fields, however, the Egyptians were more inventive. Perhaps necessity was the mother of this invention— since the Egyptians could have grown no crops without some system of irrigation. True, the Nile was and is a mighty river. Every spring it floods its banks and covers miles of farmland along either side of the river bank. But this inundation of water lasts for a few short weeks only, and for most of the year the land lying beside the Nile needs water badly if crops are to grow.

At first the ancient Egyptians brought water only to small fields close to the banks of the river. The water was lifted in pots dipped into the river and carried to the land by a simple machine called a *shaduf*. This, as can be seen in the drawing, was a form of the lever. To increase the leverage, a clay counterweight was fastened to the other end of a long pole. The workman pulled the counterweight up as he lowered the rope-suspended bucket into the water. In pulling up the filled bucket, the Egyptian workman was assisted by the clay counterweight as it sank downward with the pull of gravity.

The shaduf was a fairly efficient machine, enabling one man to raise and distribute about 600 gallons of water a day. But the area which it could irrigate was necessarily very small.

The Egyptians found a better way of bringing water to fields lying some distance from the river banks—by means of canals, dikes

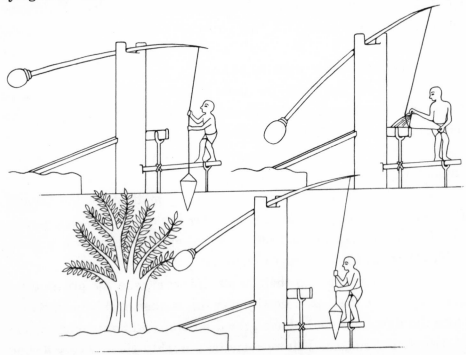

The Egyptian shaduf, used to irrigate palm tree groves, was a lever counterbalanced by a heavy weight.

and irrigation basins. Before the Old Kingdom gave way to the New Kingdom, the entire Nile River valley was a checkerboard of irrigated fields ranging from 1,000 to 40,000 acres in area. Each field was enclosed by dikes—high walls built of mud. Water was run into each field in turn, flooding the land until it was thoroughly saturated. Then the water was run out again, into one field after another, and finally returned to the river by means of canals. This system of irrigation was and is today important to Egypt. In the Old Kingdom, the district governors had as their chief title, "Digger of Canals."

Dams and aqueducts: Long before the time of the Egyptians, men must have learned how to dam up the waters of a stream with stones and clay, so that the water could be collected in back of the dam. The activities of the dam-building beavers may have inspired prehistoric men to imitate these clever little animals in regions where water was scarce. In the Old Kingdom of Egypt, dam building was fairly well advanced. In the eastern desert, today, the remains may be seen of what is probably the most ancient dam in existence. Made of rough stones held together with mortar, it is faced with limestone on the water side. It is believed this dam stored water for the workmen in a nearby alabaster quarry. This is the oldest Egyptian dam we know about, but there are many others in the country, some of them still serving to collect water for irrigation canals.

The Egyptians built dams from stones and clay.

Boats and ships: Egypt lies long and narrow along the Nile River. And so it was only natural for the Egyptians to make an early start as marine engineers. All along the Nile, in the shallow water near the banks, grow papyrus reeds. From the white, soft pith of this tough water plant the Egyptians made a crude kind of paper. But the sturdy stems of the papyrus plant could also be tied together to make rafts on which goods were floated down the Nile. Later the papyrus was woven, as in basketmaking, into reed boats. These could be guided and paddled much more easily than rafts. Still later a mast and a canvas sail made it possible to sail these boats upstream.

The reed boats were light and clumsy. If heavy loads were attempted, the boats were likely to turn over. So Egyptian carpenters, about 2500 B.C., began to make vessels in the shape of the old reed boats, but using strong wooden planks instead of papyrus as building materials. They used short lengths of lumber, steaming them to follow

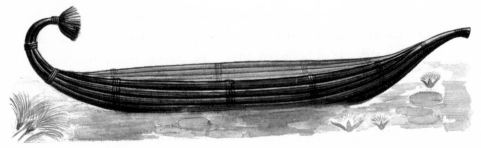

The Egyptians wove papyrus into reed boats that could be guided easily.

the curve of the boat's lines, and held the ends of the boards together in what modern carpenters call a *dovetail joint.* Wooden pins driven tightly into bored holes fastened these boards to the framework of the boat. There was no *keel,* or longer board running down the center of the underside of the boat, lengthwise. A keel gives *longitudinal strength,* and since the Egyptians knew nothing of the purpose of a keel, their boats were apt to collapse during a storm or when overloaded. The larger boats were braced against such collapses by a heavy rope running from one end of the boat to the other. The rope

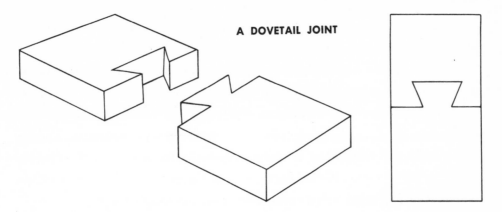

A DOVETAIL JOINT

passed over and was fastened to wooden supports in the center of the deck. The rope was kept tight by twisting a metal bar into a loop. Crude as these early Egyptian vessels were, some of them were 180 feet long and 60 feet wide, large enough to carry 120 men and seaworthy enough for ocean voyages during calm weather.

The Egyptian wooden sailing vessels had no keels, yet they were safe for ocean voyages in calm weather.

Land transportation: Because the Nile made water transportation so convenient, the Egyptians, although highly developed in other directions, were slow to use wheeled vehicles. In Mesopotamia, in China, and in other ancient civilizations of the East, carts and wagons were in common use as early as 3000 B.C. It was nearly a thousand years later before the Egyptians even saw wheeled vehicles. During the reign of Rameses III a wandering tribe from the north, bearing their goods in two-wheeled carts, visited Egypt. This visit was such an event that Egyptian artists recorded it on the king's tomb.

Tomb Painting of a Two-wheeled Cart

When Egyptians did begin to build wheeled vehicles, they used them chiefly as war chariots and as funeral hearses. Goods continued to be transported on the Nile on boats and rafts. It is odd that, although the Egyptians did not make great use of wheeled vehicles, our oldest surviving examples are chariots from Egyptian tombs dating from between 1400 and 1500 B.C. The wheels of these Egyptian chariots are made of many pieces of wood, curved and fitted to the spokes and hub with marvelous precision.

The Egyptian chariots lasted until our time because they were kept in dry, nearly airtight tombs. We know that other civilizations had wheeled vehicles long before the Egyptians. For one thing, they made small models of their carts and chariots, which probably were toys for their children. But wood, from which these early wheels were made, does not last throughout the long ages of history. Of earlier wheels, only a thin shell of petrified wood, or sometimes just the imprint of wheels in the mud, remains.

Metallurgy: Paintings on an Egyptian tomb that dates from 1440 B.C. show workmen casting a metal door for a temple. From this painting historians can reconstruct the way Egyptian metalworkers melted copper over charcoal fires fanned to great heat by leather bellows. The molten metal then was poured into a rectangular mold of slabs of baked clay.

The Egyptians also knew how to make core molds—that is, to mold a shape, such as a vase, using a core to form the hollow inside of the vase. A drawing of a typical core mold is shown on the following page. Many parts of engineering machinery and of the materials used in construction are molded. If you are interested, you can buy a kit at a hobby shop which will enable you to cast lead soldiers and similar molds, and which will also tell you how to design your own molds for special projects.

Sheet-metal working was another specialty of Egyptian craftsmen. Since the modern engineer deals with sheet metal in certain branches of his profession, such as heating and ventilating, it will be interesting to see what these ancient workmen did in sheet-metal craft. For warriors, they made helmets, shields, and armor, but most of the Egyptian metalworking was of an artistic nature. They made statues of their kings, priests, and gods, and of their sacred animals. They would cover a rough wooden framework with thousands of interlocking pieces of thin beaten metal—copper, silver, or gold. They formed the metal plates into intricate shapes by beating the metal with round-headed hammers, stopping every now and then to heat and cool the metal when it became too hard to work easily. This process of heating and cooling metal is called annealing and was probably discovered as early as 4000 B.C.

Perhaps you would like to make a small, shallow copper bowl, employing the same methods that an Egyptian craftsman might have used 4,000 years ago. When you are finished, the bowl will make a

A CORE MOLD

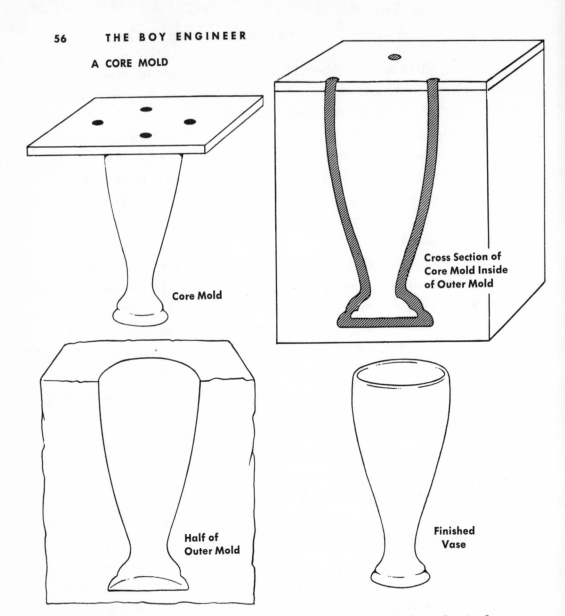

Core Mold

Cross Section of
Core Mold Inside
of Outer Mold

Half of
Outer Mold

Finished
Vase

fine present for your mother, sister, or best girl friend. And you will have gained a feeling for metalwork that no amount of reading would accomplish.

Begin your bowl by obtaining a piece of sheet copper about 8 inches square. With a compass set to a radius of 3½ inches or a piece of string of that length tied to a pencil, mark a circle 7 inches in diameter on the face of the copper. Cut around the circle carefully with a pair of metal shears.

Egyptian Craftsmen Fashioned Bowls Almost Sixty Centuries Ago.

Your bowl must have a flat bottom on which to rest, otherwise it will rock at the slightest touch. To mark off this flat bottom, mark another circle 3 inches in diameter in the center of your flat copper disk.

Take a ball-peen hammer and, using the round part of the head, strike a series of blows all around the *outside* of the circle you have marked for the flat bottom of your bowl, holding the metal against a small anvil or the jaws of a workshop vise. As you hammer around the circle work outward in a series of longer and longer spirals toward the edge of the copper disk. But be sure to stop hammering about a half inch from the actual edge.

As you hammer, you will notice that the metal is stretching and bending into bowl shape. From time to time, you will notice that the copper becomes hard to work. When this happens you will have to stop and anneal the metal. Take a strong pair of tongs or a big pair of pliers, and, wearing gloves to protect your hands, hold the copper carefully over a gas flame until the copper turns dark brown. Then put it aside to cool on some scorchproof surface (the sidewalk will do), until it regains its copper color.

You may have to work over your bowl three or four times, spiraling outward from the flat bottom to near the outside edge, before your bowl has been beaten into the proper shape. Finally, you can hammer out any minor bumps or other imperfections by holding the bowl against a curved part of your anvil or vise and beating the metal with the *flat* head of the hammer. This finishing step is called *planishing*.

Polish your bowl to a gleaming finish with fine steel wool and protect this finish with a coat of spar varnish or clear lacquer.

Soldering and welding: You have seen your father or the TV repairman solder wires together with a soldering iron and something he called flux solder. Have you ever wondered what happens to bring the two wire ends together in a tight joint?

When you heat the end of a wire, you increase the surface tension until the end of the wire melts and runs into a blob of liquid metal. The temperature at which this melting starts is called the fusion point, and it varies with different metals. Some metals melt at low heat, others have an extremely high fusion point.

You might think that if you laid two wire ends together and heated them to the fusion point, the ends would run together and form a joint when cool. What actually happens, however, is that the ends *draw back from each other* as they reach the fusion point.

Nor can the two wires be joined by heating and pounding the softened metal in all cases. Wrought iron can be joined in this way, but not most other metals.

But copper and other metals can be joined when any other metal, or alloy of the same metal, with a *lower* melting point than the pieces to be joined, is allowed to flow between the pieces. Upon cooling, the pieces will be joined tightly together. Various chemicals, applied in paste form to the metal to be joined, are used before soldering to seal out air and help make a firmer bond between the metals. This chemical sealer is called the *flux*.

Historians believe ancient craftsmen first discovered the soldering principle when working with gold. Pure gold has a low melting point, but gold which contains particles of silver or copper, melts at a still lower temperature. Without really knowing why, the ancient metalworkers discovered that these coarser grades of gold could be used to solder finer pieces of gold together. Later they discovered that certain grades of copper (containing impurities of zinc) could be used to solder copper parts together.

The Egyptians were clever in using solder for their metalwork. A canopy over the tomb of a queen, buried about 2500 B.C., is supported by copper poles fastened into sockets under the canopy with silver solder.

As engineers, the ancient Egyptians were well-skilled in some techniques and very primitive in others, compared to other civilizations of the same period. Although the building and use of wheeled vehicles was much farther advanced in Mesopotamia, where chariots were needed on the deserts, certainly no other people of the time were better structural engineers than the pyramid-building Egyptians.

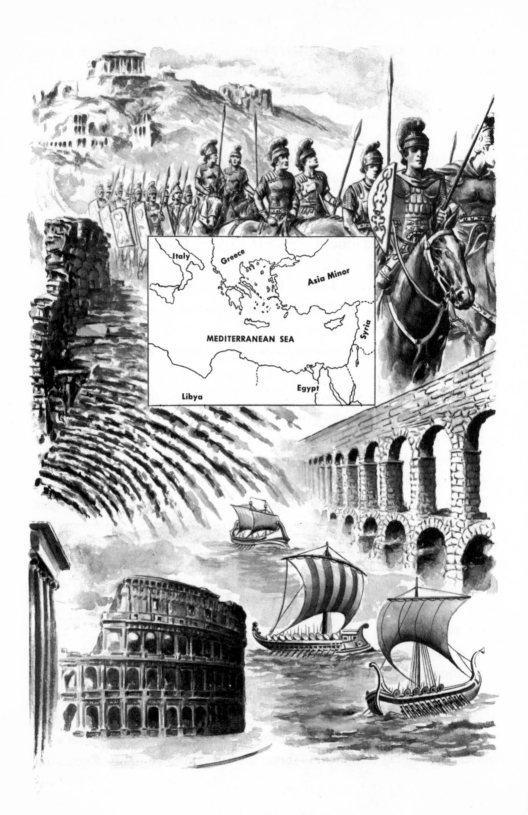

Italy Greece

Asia Minor

MEDITERRANEAN SEA

Syria

Libya Egypt

CHAPTER THREE

ENGINEERING MARVELS OF THE GREEKS AND ROMANS

MODERN engineers owe a large debt to the great civilizations of Greece and Rome. Engineers and architects have hailed the Parthenon and other great Greek public buildings as among the most architecturally perfect of man's creations. Yet there is something odd, and at the same time very significant, about all Greek buildings. From the humblest home to the largest public auditorium, they all rose from a simple rectangle. The walls were supported by posts and beams, a method of construction the Greeks had learned from the Egyptians and other older civilizations. The slanting (pitched) roofs were formed by a ridgepole and rafters, as many of our houses are today. There were porches, supported by columns which sometimes ran around all four sides of the rectangle. In the larger buildings, interior columns helped support the weight of the roof.

This was the simple, fixed rectangular form. Yet no two Greek buildings were exactly alike, because the Greeks were artists as well as engineers. You can convince yourself of this by trying to make a drawing from the picture of the Parthenon included here. You will find that the beauty of the building depends almost entirely on the proportions of the various parts. Without these very slight but skillful changes in proportion, Greek buildings would have had no more beautiful dimensions than a modern one-car garage which starts from the same rectangular plan.

Let us take, for example, the Parthenon. This famous Greek temple is, basically, a rectangle 100 feet wide and 228 feet long. It has 46 Doric columns, each 34 feet high. To the eye, it may seem that these columns are composed of perfectly straight vertical lines. Actually, however, they curve. They measure 6 feet 3 inches at the base, widen slightly as they rise, and then gradually taper to 4 feet

The Parthenon is a famous Greek temple on the Acropolis.

10 inches in width at the top. You will notice that these columns have grooves, called *flutings*. These flutings are wider at the bottom of the columns, narrowing as they reach the top. But they do *not* vary in depth. Such subtle refinements as these are responsible for the fine shadow effects produced in Greek buildings.

Even the horizontal lines of the Parthenon and other great Greek structures are not truly horizontal. The steps leading up to the temple, for instance, are not level, but rise toward the center in a gentle arc. The Greeks did this because they knew so much about lines and planes and the optical illusions they can create. They knew that if the Parthenon steps *were* horizontal, they would appear to sag in the center because of the extreme breadth of the stairs.

The Greeks made great use of the simple machines in their engineering. They cut the outline of a building block into a wall of marble and then split it away by driving wooden wedges into the cut and then wetting the wedges. The pressure of the water-swollen wedges was enough to split off the building stone along the cuts. The Greeks did not smooth their blocks at the quarry as the ancient Egyptians had done—instead the Greeks left knobs on the stone under which levers could be placed to pry the stones out of the quarry.

Sometimes the building stones were hauled to the building site in ox-drawn carts. At other times the Greeks put the blocks on wooden cradles, under which they placed long rollers to serve as wheels. Still another method was to enclose the block in a round drum of wood and roll the whole thing to the job. Derricks and compound pulleys were used to handle the blocks of stone at the site of the building project.

Few people realize, when looking at pictures of the beautiful stone temples of the Greeks, that their building engineers used a great deal of iron in their work. Where the Egyptians had used stones so massive that they held together by their own weight, the Greeks cut much smaller stones and clamped them together with bars of iron. These bars were bent at right angles at each end, and these ends went into holes drilled into the stone. There were grooves cut into the stone between these holes so that the bars would be flush with the face of the stone. Often foundations, crossbeams over doorways, and rafter beams were reinforced with iron bars to increase safety. The iron clamps and the iron-bar reinforcements were sealed in with hot lead. The iron was probably treated with tallow to make it rust-resistant, but today most of the iron in the ancient Greek ruins has rusted away entirely.

Thus the Greeks seem to have been the first engineers to realize that while stone is strong and durable, it does not have the tensile strength (stretching strength) of iron. Tensile strength is measured by the amount of weight necessary to *break* a given material.

HOW BLOCKS OF STONE WERE CLAMPED TOGETHER

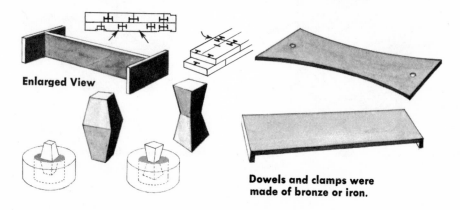

Enlarged View

Dowels and clamps were made of bronze or iron.

A class of master workmen of great engineering skill appeared among the Greeks. The most skilled of these were called *architectrons*, and one of these was in charge of every building project. They directed the workmen, working from specifications cut on a stone tablet which would correspond to the blueprints of the modern engineer. On this tablet the materials to be used, sizes of stones, dimensions of the building and its parts, location and number of windows, doors, steps, and other details were cut.

The Greeks were among the first to plan cities. The cities built during the later period of their civilization had wide main avenues and cross streets, forming rectangular blocks in which were built the public buildings, temples, theaters, homes, athletic fields, monuments and parks.

The streets were paved, and the water supply for each block or square came from a central fountain. These street fountains were fed from springs high in the mountains. Ditches and pipes carried the water to a reservoir near the city, and more clay pipes led from the reservoir to the street fountains. In the finer homes of the rich or the influential Greek citizens, water pipes supplied bathrooms and water taps.

HERO'S STEAM TURBINE

Heat made the water inside the ball turn to steam, which escaped through the bent tube. The jets of steam made the ball turn.

The bathroom of a rich man's home in ancient Greece was almost as fine as that of the average American today. Greek ruins have been found which contain built-in tubs, with an overhead spout connected to spring-fed pipes from the hills. There was even a tile drain at the bottom of the tub.

Yet, although their streets were paved and there were a few short roads leading to quarries and wharves, the Greeks were not great road builders.

Curiously, the Greek world possessed skills and ideas which were almost wholly neglected by the Greek engineers themselves. Those gifts included geometry, which Euclid organized into a body of mathematics, and the many scientific experiments and theories by Archimedes and other Greek philosophers. They may be said to have laid the foundations for modern science, upon which the modern engineer depends so heavily for advancements in his field. The Greek engineers, however, made little use of these things. Their engineering feats were mainly improvements on techniques they had learned from the Egyptians and other earlier peoples, or which they had learned from experience, rather than from scientific theory or experiment.

For example, while the Greek workmen were building their classic temples with oxcarts, levers, and pulleys, a Greek scholar named Hero was trying to develop a steam turbine. A drawing of Hero's turbine is reproduced here. Other Greeks were experimenting with water clocks, force pumps and similar mechanical devices. But there was no connection, as yet, with practical engineering.

The Greeks made only a small contribution to marine engineering. Their ships were much like those of the Egyptians, with square sails and with little ability to sail against the wind. They did, however, make their ships broader in the beam (wider) in order that they might safely carry much larger cargoes than the narrow Egyptian ships.

In military engineering, however, the Greeks made some notable advances in weapons, the first since the spear and bow and arrow. Most of these mechanical weapons were invented by Archimedes, whom we usually think of as a mathematician and scientist. It was he who established the laws of the lever and other simple machines, although men had been using such machines without knowing their laws for thousands of years. It was Archimedes, too, who established other principles of physics which engineers use in their work today. One of these was the discovery that an object placed in water displaces an amount of water equal to the volume of the object, and the object "loses" in weight by the amount of the water displaced.

But Archimedes, who studied at the famous Egyptian school of mathematics in Alexandria, was also an inventor and practical engineer. His war machines were responsible for many Greek victories in battle. One of these was a battering ram—a huge beam mounted on movable arms so that it could be swung back and forth inside a wheeled frame. A few men working the battering ram could run the frame to the side of a wall and batter an opening through the stones.

Another weapon developed by Archimedes was the catapult. This was a springy lever which was pulled back and loaded with a huge stone, and then released to send the stone flying hundreds of feet.

You can make a catapult of your own that will be a lot of fun

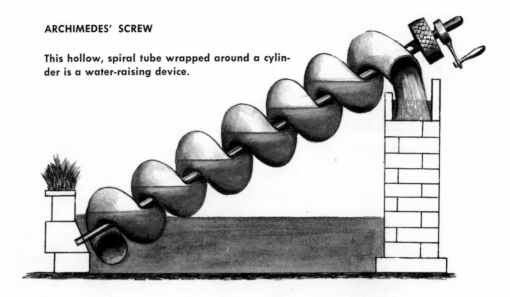

ARCHIMEDES' SCREW

This hollow, spiral tube wrapped around a cylinder is a water-raising device.

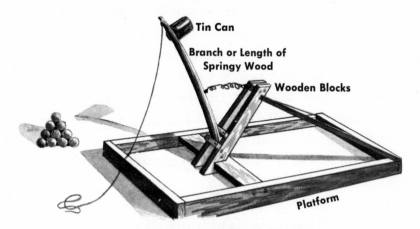

Tin Can

Branch or Length of
Springy Wood

Wooden Blocks

Platform

MAKE YOUR OWN SNOWBALL CATAPULT

for target practice or for use in mock battles with your friends. First, select the springiest tree branch or strip of wood you can find. Mount this on a sturdy wooden base at an angle, as shown in the drawing. Next, take a tin can, and nail or screw the can to the spring arm of your catapult. In winter, you can load your catapult with snowballs. In summer it would be safer to use cheap rubber balls for ammunition —rocks fired from your catapult can be dangerous. To fire, you simply pull the spring arm down as far as you can and let go.

THE ROMANS AS ENGINEERS

The Romans were the only ancient people to excel in almost every branch of engineering. They originated very little. Instead, they borrowed from everyone else, and then did the job better than any other nation. As we know, the Romans were conquerors. They conquered peoples and took over the administration of the captive nations, blending their own engineering techniques with those of the people they conquered. In building, they borrowed from the Egyptians and Greeks and erected larger and stronger buildings. They were excellent road builders—some Roman roads that were built thousands of years ago are carrying automobile traffic today. Their planned cities not only had paved streets, but sewer systems as well. They had the best system of aqueducts for water supply that the world had seen up to that time. The Romans were such excellent engineers that it is worthwhile to examine their engineering accomplishments in detail.

Building. As we have said, the Romans were able to build larger and taller structures than the Greeks. They were able to do this because of their use of the arch. The Greeks seem to have known about the arch, but for some reason seldom used it in their buildings. They passed up one of the engineering devices for distributing loads in so doing.

One of the early civilizations which made use of the arch in building was the Mycenaean, which preceded the Greek. The principal city, Mycenae, was on the mainland of what is now Greece. In their palaces and temples, the Mycenaeans used a crude kind of arch, called the false arch, or "corbelled" arch.

You can see for yourself how an arch is self-supporting by constructing a rough imitation of the corbelled arch of the Mycenaeans. Take a set of child's blocks, or some dominoes, or anything else of this kind. Start with two blocks set apart the distance you want your little archway to be. Now put another block on top of each of the first two, but let one-fourth of the second block stick out over the first block toward the center of the arch-to-be. Continue piling blocks

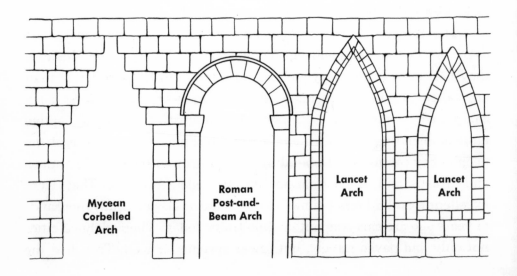

Mycean
Corbelled
Arch

Roman
Post-and-
Beam Arch

Lancet
Arch

Lancet
Arch

on either side, each time leaving a projection of one-fourth of a block, until two blocks meet at the top of the arch.

You will find the rough arch you have made is self-supporting and fairly sturdy in the face of vibration. You can pile quite a few blocks on top of the arch without disturbing it.

Next, you can contrast the strength of the arch as used by the Mycenaeans and improved by the Romans with the post-and-beam system of building used by the Egyptians and the Greeks. With the same blocks, build two vertical pillars the same height as your arch, and place a ruler across the top to serve as the crossbeam, or lintel. You will find this setup is shaky—not nearly as sturdy as the arch of blocks you built. That is because a crossbeam does not transfer to the side columns a great deal of the weight it must support. An arch, on the other hand, transfers practically all the weight it supports to the side columns.

The Romans took the rough corbelled arch of the Mycenaeans and refined it into the true arch. There are several kinds of arches, as may be seen in the drawings on the opposite page. The most common arch is a segment of a circle. Other arches, such as the horseshoe arch and the lancet arch, are elliptical—that is, their sides are the parts of two circles drawn from separate center points. Get your compass and see for yourself how many shapes an arch can take.

Engineers and architects have definite names for the various parts of an arch, as made up by the stones especially shaped for each part of the curves of an arch. The center block is called the *keystone*. The keystone and the stones on either side of the keystone make up the *crown*, or highest part of the arch. The stones running from the crown to the lowest stone of the arch are called the *haunches*. The lowest stone is called either the *springer* or the *skewback*. Just below the ends of the arch proper is a stone known as the *impost*.

The Romans made great use of the arch in their buildings, aqueducts, underground vaults and bridges. The arch continues to be in wide use today. You can understand how a series of arches, side by side, transfers weight from a long span to a series of arched sections, each resting on its own foundation footings. Dome-shaped structures can be made by arches which intersect at right angles.

As for their building techniques, the Romans, like the Greeks, at first joined their building stones with clamps of iron. Then, later, they began laying up walls of smaller, irregularly shaped stones that were held together with a mortar of lime and sand instead of iron clamps. They confidently built a number of large apartment houses, called *insulae,* for the poor people of Rome. They found, however, that in a few years the lime-and-sand mortar dried and crumbled. The huge apartment buildings often collapsed, sometimes killing a number of the people who lived in them.

Still later, Roman builders added a third ingredient to their lime and mortar. This ingredient was a fine ash left after eruptions of the volcano, Vesuvius. The lime-mortar-volcanic ash mixture made a fine mortar—in fact it was as strong or stronger than cement today. The Romans called their cement *pozzuolana.* The Smithsonian Institution in Washington, D.C., has a section of sewer pipe made of Roman pozzuolana. You may see it there if you ever get the chance to visit the nation's capital. The pipe is stronger now than when the Romans laid it underground almost 2,000 years ago. In fact, chemical action over the years has turned it into stone.

With such strong cement to bind their materials, the Romans were able to build with bricks as well as stones. They used bricks in all shapes: square, oblong, triangular and curved, the curved ones

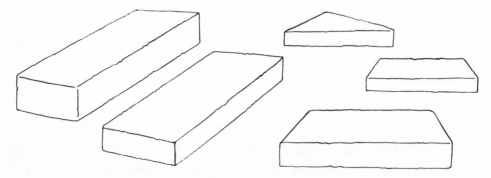

Roman bricks had many shapes.

being used to build round supporting columns and smokestacks. Modern engineers and contractors today use a long, wide brick called *roman* brick.

In erecting brick structures, the Romans built two walls side by side, and filled the space between with small stones, bits of broken pottery and mortar. They also strengthened the walls with *header* stones or bricks running across the double wall of bricks at intervals.

Water supply. The Romans had another use for the arch—to support the ducts used to carry water down from the hills surrounding Rome, over many miles of rolling valleys and ridges, and into the streets and houses of their cities.

The pipes or ducts carrying the water were laid on top of these

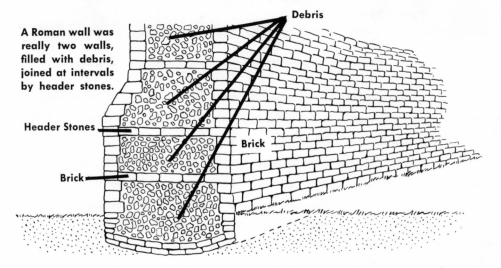

A Roman wall was really two walls, filled with debris, joined at intervals by header stones.

Header Stones

Brick

Debris

Brick

high aqueducts. Arches were ideal for supporting the aqueducts for two reasons. Each arch could carry its share of the burden safely. Secondly, the arches could easily be varied in height so that the aqueduct could follow the rise and fall of the land, and also maintain an over-all slope so that a smooth flow of water from hills to city would result. If you study the drawing of an aqueduct on the following page you will see why this is so.

The Romans knew the principle of the inverted siphon, by which water could be transported underground, following the contours of

Roman aqueducts were so sturdily built that many are still standing today.

the land, under pressure. But the arched aqueducts were easier to build and repair, and their gradual slope lessened the danger of the water pipes bursting under too much pressure.

All the principal cities of the Empire had aqueducts, and Rome itself had 11 of them, from 10 to 60 miles long. It is estimated from ancient records that these aqueducts delivered 220 million gallons of water to Rome every day. The water was piped to the public fountains in the streets, to which Roman slaves went every day for household supplies of water. Water was also piped to public baths, to laundries and to cloth-dyeing mills. No water was supposed to be supplied to private homes, although a few wealthy citizens bribed inspectors to have pipes lead to taps in their houses, and others secretly tapped the mains themselves.

Bridges. The Romans were builders of many bridges—but it cannot be said that all of their bridges were great or long lasting. Most of the Roman bridges—even the better ones—have been swept away, while many of the buildings, aqueducts and roads still stand, and a few are still in use. The Romans spanned wide streams with bridges consisting of a series of arches. But they had many troubles with these arched bridges. They sank the heavy pier ends of the arches into the bedrock of the river. But the many piers needed blocked much of the channel of the river, and increased the strength and rate of flow of the current between the piers. These conditions in time weakened the masonry, so that the arches were often swept away, particularly during floods.

Over narrow streams, the Roman engineers often built a "muleback" bridge—that is, a bridge consisting of a single arch spanning the river from one bank to the other. The roadway from bank to bank went up over the arch, and crossing such a bridge was like going up, over, and down a steep hill.

In only a few instances did the Roman engineers use the modern method of sinking piers by means of a cofferdam. In this method, a watertight framework of piles was driven deep into the riverbed to bedrock. Then the water was pumped out of the framework, or cofferdam. In this space, heavy piers of timber or masonry could be built.

From your studies in history you have perhaps learned how the

The Roman "muleback" bridge was a single arch that spanned a river from bank to bank.

Romans conquered a large area of the civilized world. This explains why Roman bridges, roads and aqueducts can be found all over the Middle East, Europe and even in the British Isles. Many are in ruins now, but enough of them remain to tell us that the Romans built many kinds of bridges. From an engineering standpoint, some were good and some were bad. Some of them, it must be remembered, were probably intended to be merely temporary structures over which Roman troops and supplies could be transported.

In Rome itself, six of seven bridges built in the time of the Caesars are still in use across the Tiber River. They have been repaired frequently during the centuries since Roman engineers first erected their semicircular arches. The highest and longest bridge the ancient Romans probably ever built still carries traffic over the Tagus River at Alcantara, in Spain. This bridge is nearly 200 feet high, and has six great arches that support a roadway 600 feet long.

Roads. The Romans may have received more credit for their road-building ability than they actually deserve. As with their bridges, not all Roman roads were good, even when their limited tools and knowledge are taken into consideration. Archaeologists have discovered roads built by earlier peoples which were better than some built, centuries later, by the Romans. It is known that the Romans copied many of the methods of these earlier civilizations. And sometimes they did not make their roads as well as they knew how for the same reasons that engineers today often build a lightly traveled country road with a far less durable roadbed than they construct when building a superhighway.

Nevertheless, the Romans, at the height of their power, had a well-developed system of roads extending in all directions over more than 50,000 miles—to Egypt, Greece, China and over the Alps into Germany. The greatest of the Roman roads was the Appian Way, begun by a statesman of the Roman Republic, Appius Claudius Caecus, in 312 B.C. It was later extended by other Roman leaders. Called the "Queen of Roads," the Appian Way ran from Rome all along the southeast coast of Italy.

We must not think of these ancient Roman roads as being as wide as those to which we are accustomed. Only the Appian Way—18 feet wide—came close to the width of our roads. Most single lane chariot roads were 4 feet wide, and the two-lane *via* was only 8 feet wide. There were paved roads for pedestrians and horsemen which were only three feet wide—more like our sidewalks—and there were many paved footpaths only a foot wide.

Different materials and different methods were used in building these ancient Roman roads, but the use of certain engineering practices was common to all of them. All were crowned — that is, the

The Appian Way, begun in 312 B.C., was 18 feet wide and ran from Rome all along the southeast coast of Italy. It is still an important Italian roadway.

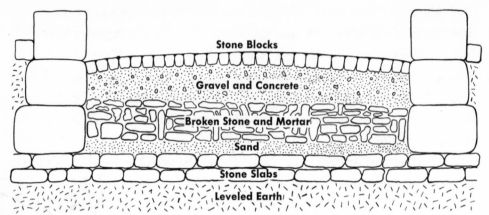

CROSS SECTION OF A ROMAN ROAD

center was rounded up slightly—so that water could drain off on either side of the roadway. The street in front of your house—perhaps even your own driveway—is crowned in this way for drainage purposes. As in modern streets and roads, this drainage was carried away at the sides in ditches and culverts, so that water would not undermine the roadbed foundation.

Roman roadbeds were 8 feet deep, which means that some *vias* were as deep as they were wide. Few of our modern roads—even the great superhighways—are more than a foot deep. The Romans began their roads by leveling off the earth. Then for their better roads, they laid a foundation of 2-foot-thick stone slabs, joined with mortar and topped with an even layer of sand. Next comes a layer of broken stone and mortar, followed by a layer of fine gravel and concrete, and finally the surface layer of hard stone blocks, each about 2 feet square and 5 inches thick. These surface blocks were laid close together and provided a fairly smooth highway. If you ever have occasion to visit Washington, D.C., you should visit the offices of the United States Bureau of Public Roads. Here you can see a model of the Appian Way, which was built in the fashion just described.

Although the Romans used cement to bind the stones of the sublayers of their roads, it does not appear that they ever thought to pour cement into forms to make slabs of concrete, as modern engineers do in making many roads today. Nor did the Romans ever hit upon the idea of making roads of asphalt, as we do today, although the material was right at hand. The Romans had a natural asphalt in bitumen, which they used in some building structures, but never for roads. Perhaps our modern engineers, faced with rising road construction costs and the need for more and better roads, are also overlooking the use of some material which we have on hand. Perhaps you will be able to think of a material which might be used in building better and cheaper roads. If you do, your future as an engineer will be a bright one.

WITH the fall of the Roman Empire there began a thousand-year period in history called the Middle Ages. They are full of interest to the engineer, because it was during these thousand years, roughly from 400 to 1400, that some important steps were taken in engineering progress.

The achievements of the Greeks and the Romans in their periods of glory were great indeed. But behind their beautiful temples and buildings, their mighty dams, roads and bridges, canals and aqueducts, was the back-breaking toil of human beings. Both these ancient civilizations knew and used the simple machines. But operating each of these machines was a sweating laborer, usually a slave. A thousand men might die in the building of one temple or tomb.

True, man did succeed in shifting part of the work to animals. Oxen—slow, dull and awkward as they are—were used to turn the levers of mills, grindstones and crude saws, and to lift ore from mine shafts. Then with the invention of a harness for horses (horses would have choked to death if harnessed to yokes as oxen were), those swifter, more intelligent and more willing creatures came into use as work animals.

It was during the Middle Ages, too, that men began to make good use of two natural sources of power that are still important today —water and wind. These are known to engineers as *prime movers*.

Crude water wheels, known to have been used in ancient India, were rediscovered by the Romans in the last days of their empire. Let us see how these crude water wheels were improved, stage by stage, until they became the mighty modern turbines which generate electricity from waterpower.

The ancient water wheels were laid on their sides in a river or

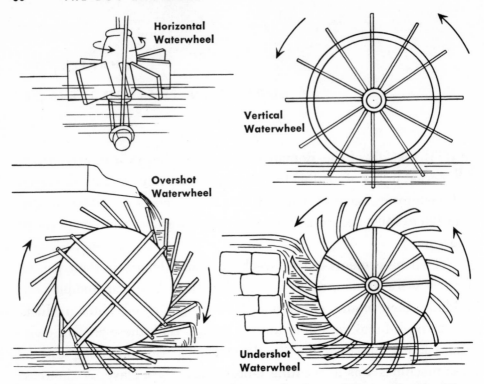

stream, with the axle on which they revolved standing vertically. They could not have been very efficient. You can see from the drawing that most of the wheel was moving against water which tended to *resist* the turning of the wheel, while only a small arc of the wheel, at any given time, was being moved around by the force of the current.

Later it was found that efficiency was greater if the wheel was set on edge in the water, with the revolving axle horizontal, so that the part of the wheel not being moved by the current would be free to turn in the air.

This was a much better kind of wheel, but like the vertical water wheel, its speed and power depended entirely on the swiftness of the current in the particular stream. Another forward step was taken when someone invented an *overshot* water wheel. The water, falling from either a natural waterfall or from a sluice artificially arranged to create a waterfall, struck the top of the wheel, thus adding the force of momentum to that of its mass.

At first these overshot water wheels took the force of the water on the outside of the wheel. But it was discovered that the bottom of the wheel met resistance from the current as it turned inward against the flow of the water at the bottom. The water-wheel engineers then arranged matters so that the water would strike on the inside of the wheel, turning the wheel in the direction of the current below and eliminating that resistance. This was called a *pitchback*.

The blades of water wheels, which had been practically flat at first, later became more curved, in order to obtain as much energy as possible from the falling water, and then to throw it clear of the blades so that it could not offer any resistance beneath.

You may wish to try your hand at building a water wheel. This project requires eight curved pieces of wood bandsawed from 1-inch lumber. The perspective details on this page give the dimensions and show the basic construction of the wheel. The ends of the bandsawed

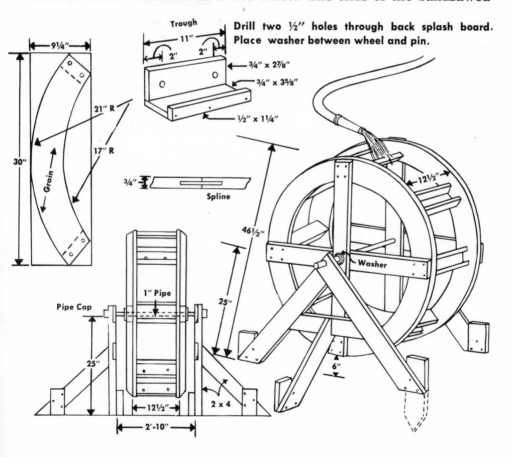

segments are butted together and joined with a spline and bolts. The bolts also fasten the segments to a half-lapped X-brace of 2 x 4's to form each side of the wheel. A length of 1-inch pipe serves as the wheel axle, which is supported by wooden brackets staked to the ground. Short sections cut from oversized pipe can be used to provide bushings for the axle. The eight buckets which are nailed between the sides of the wheel are simple wooden troughs. Two holes are drilled in the back of each trough to drain off excess water as the wheel revolves. Water can be fed directly to the wheel by means of a garden hose, or you may wish to construct a long, inclined trough.

Toward the close of the Middle Ages, engineers developed the windmill. In Holland, and in other wind-swept low countries of Europe, the windmill was a better and simpler source of power than the water wheel. At first the windmill was little more than four arms bearing huge, framed cloth sails to catch the wind. The arms turned an axle connected to the grindstone or the saw inside the mill building. In order to put these sails into the wind, the entire building had to be turned in the right direction. In about 1500, however, windmill builders developed the bonnet windmill, whose vanes could be turned into the wind without turning the whole structure. While much lighter,

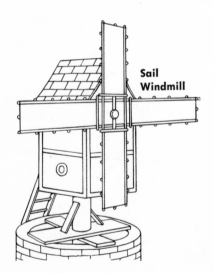

Sail
Windmill

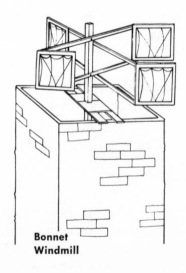

Bonnet
Windmill

the bonnet windmill developed more power than the cumbersome sail windmills.

Both the windmill and the water wheel were products of the Middle Ages, but their importance in the production of power has extended to the present day. Even now, in the age of electric, diesel, gasoline engine and steam power, the prime movers are important power sources. Modern impulse reaction turbines, generating electrical energy at huge dams throughout the world, are outgrowths of the early water wheels. And windmills still generate electricity and pump water on farms and ranches all over the globe.

The windmill harnesses the energy of the wind.

In the drawing of a typical farm windmill, it is easy to follow the transmission of wind power and the changes made in the speed and direction of this energy. The wind turns the vanes of the windmill rapidly, but small gears on the shaft, connecting with larger ones, slow down the speed, thereby increasing the power. Rocker arms on the outer edges of the large gears change the rotary motion into a reciprocating, up-and-down motion of the long rod. This rod pumps water from the farm well usually dug below the frame of the windmill. The workings of a pump are described at the end of this chapter.

Another achievement belonging to the Middle Ages and involving the use of wind power was the discovery that ships could sail *against* the wind. The fixed square sails of ancient times needed the wind directly behind them, or nearly so, if the ship was to move in the right direction. Ship captains often had to wait weeks for a favorable wind, and sailing schedules were anything but certain.

The invention that solved this problem was the triangular *lateen* sail, fixed to a movable yardarm so that the sail could be positioned at nearly any point in a circle around the mast.

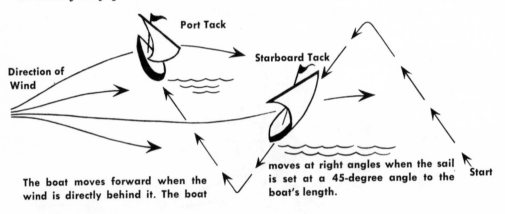

Port Tack

Starboard Tack

Direction of Wind

Start

moves at right angles when the sail is set at a 45-degree angle to the boat's length.

The boat moves forward when the wind is directly behind it. The boat

The drawings on this page show us what happens to a boat equipped with a lateen sail when the wind is blowing in various directions. With the wind directly behind the boat, of course, the progress of the boat is forward, in the same direction as the wind. When the sail is placed at right angles to this direction, the tendency of the boat to turn is overcome by setting the rudder to the same side of the boat as the sail. With the sail fixed at a 45-degree angle to the length of the boat, it can be sailed in a direction at right angles to the direction of the wind. Here again, the tendency of the boat to turn is overcome by the rudder and the long centerboard or keel which sticks deep into the water below the boat and helps to hold it steady on its course.

Sailing directly against the wind is a little more complicated. The sail is set at only a very slight angle, and the boat proceeds in a series of zig-zags, in a maneuver sailors call *tacking*. The angle of the sail is altered at intervals, each interval being called a *leg* of the tack.

There are several things which combine to make the sailing boat move forward at an angle despite the fact that the wind is blowing in the opposite direction. In the first place, the general shape of the boat, its deep keel, and the setting of the rudder tend to make it move forward when the sail is set at a slight angle to the wind. In addition,

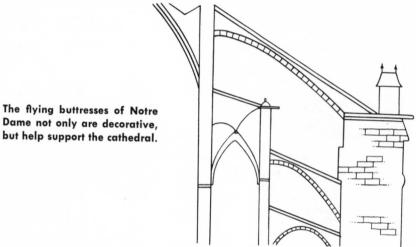

The flying buttresses of Notre Dame not only are decorative, but help support the cathedral.

as the boat moves forward, it creates a wind of its own, just by sailing through the air. This combination of the angle of the *true wind* against the sail and the wind the boat makes results in an *apparent wind*. It is the apparent wind that really drives the boat.

Building methods progressed during the Middle Ages, particularly in the construction of churches. This was a period when the church was a strong influence in the daily lives of most people, since the Roman Empire had crumbled, and most civil governments had fallen into the hands of a number of petty, weak rulers. Medieval engineers built some of the largest and most beautiful cathedrals the world has ever seen. Today, when modern architects build in the Romanesque or Gothic style, they do no more than copy these great cathedrals.

One of the most famous and beautiful of these cathedrals is Notre Dame, standing on an island in the Seine River in the heart of Paris. Notre Dame is an important landmark in engineering, because it was here that the *flying buttress* was first used in a practical way. The Romans had made good use of the arch, but they had never solved one fault of the arch—its tendency to weaken the walls of a tall building. In dealing with this problem, medieval engineers took away from the arch most of its responsibility for supporting the roof. Instead, they put the load on tall, strong piers, placed between the arches and standing a little way out from the building. But sometimes

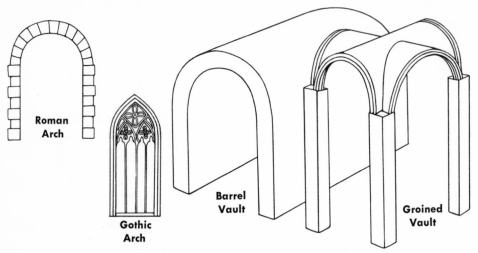

Roman Arch

Gothic Arch

Barrel Vault

Groined Vault

these tall piers collapsed under too great an internal thrust from the weight of the roof. The flying buttress, joined to the main wall by a half arch at the point where the internal thrust must be taken, solved this problem. The drawing on page 85 shows how a flying buttress works.

The arch, as used by the Romans and as it appeared in Romanesque cathedrals after the fall of the Roman Empire, was rounded. In Gothic architecture, however, the stronger pointed arch was used almost exclusively, because it allowed the cathedrals to rise higher than round arches would permit.

The earliest cathedrals had wooden truss roofs. But so many cathedrals were destroyed by fire that builders developed the stone *barrel vault* and, still later, the *groined vault*, which is made up of two barrel vaults intersecting at right angles.

We have been speaking of medieval engineers—but in the Middle Ages there was yet no such word. The men who built the cathedrals were simply masons—but they were extremely skilled in their trade and highly artistic in their approach. They had an amazing knowledge of the properties of the stone, iron, timber and mortar with which they worked. And while these masons were not called engineers, the things they accomplished would make them worthy of the name today.

During the Middle Ages there was little travel or exchange of goods between the countries of Europe and Asia. There were few roads and bridges built during this period in history. The old Roman roads were kept up, but few new roads were built, and these were of dirt or loose stones. The Roman bridges were repaired, and a few new ones were built. Julius Caesar had built a stone bridge across the Rhine River, but that had been washed away after centuries of use. The Emperor Charlemagne in about A.D. 800, replaced it with a huge wooden bridge which burned shortly after it was completed.

Another grand plan of Charlemagne's that came to a poor end was the building of a canal to link the Danube with the Rhine. Thousands of men began digging a channel 300 feet wide. Charlemagne and his engineers, however, had little knowledge of the engineering principles involved in digging a canal. As they dug in the swampy ground, the banks caved in behind them a day or two later. Finally, the enterprise was abandoned. It was a long time before a canal linking the Danube and the Rhine ever was actually built. The wars

Medieval Ships at Antwerp Harbor

that raged over Europe for more than a thousand years made Charlemagne's idea seem impractical, even dangerous, to the countries the
canal would link by water traffic. The Neckar Canal now linking these
great rivers of Europe was not begun until the 1930's, and construction
was halted during World War II.

The knowledge of how to sail against the wind, discovered by
mariners of the Middle Ages, made longer voyages possible and called
for bigger ships. The bigger ships needed deeper harbors, and docks
in which they could be repaired when they needed painting or suffered
damage below the water line.

In the days of the ancient empires, ships were so small that they
could be brought up to shore at high tide and pulled up on the beach.
Only a few men were needed to turn them on their sides to make repairs
on the bottom. But the larger ships of the Middle Ages could not
even be brought close to land except in places where there was a
natural harbor. At many seaports, harbors had to be dug out of
natural bays along the coast or at the mouths of rivers emptying into
the sea. Ships needed harbors where they could be anchored in quiet
water, and wharves for the loading and unloading of cargo. A harbor
had to be protected from sea waves either by natural projections of
land between the harbor and the sea, or by man-made barriers called
breakwaters.

The first docks for ship repair were fairly simple, but they could
be built only where there was a great difference in the levels of the
water at high and low tide. At high tide, the ship would be floated in
over a sort of wooden cradle set in the bottom of a harbor. At low
tide, as the water moved away from the shore, the ship would settle
into the cradle with its bottom out of the water. Before the next high
tide, a wall of clay and brush and timber was built around the cradle.
Within this wall, on land that was only fairly dry, repairs could be
made on the bottom of the ship. When the work was done, the crude
wall was broken, and the next high tide would lift the ship from
its cradle, ready to sail again.

The tides made it difficult to load and unload cargoes at the wharves, since the ship rose and fell twice a day on the tides. Docks with walls and a floor, like a big box, with a gate at the seaward side, overcame this difficulty. A ship was brought in at high tide, and as the tide dropped, the gate was closed and water remained in the dock to keep the ship riding at the same level at the wharf side.

After this sort of dock had been invented, it was only another step to pump the water from the dock and leave the ship's bottom exposed for painting and repairs. Such a special dock for repairs is called a *drydock*.

The pump was one of the most important machines developed in the Middle Ages. It was used not only in ship repair docks, but to dry out mines, to irrigate fields and to supply towns with water. Perhaps this would be a good place to examine the different kinds of pumps, and find out how they work.

Even the most city-bound boy must occasionally have seen water pumped from a well on a farm or golf course. This is the simplest kind of pump—a lift pump. The handle of the pump operates a piston which slides up and down in a cylinder connected to a pipe which reaches down the well as far as the water.

You will notice, when you operate a real pump, that the water does not start flowing until you have pumped for some time. That is because the first strokes of the lift pump force air out of the cylinder and create a partial vacuum. The water at the bottom of the well starts up the pipe because of the pulling power of the vacuum created by the lift pump. It is the same thing that happens when we create a partial vacuum in a soda straw by sucking on the end—the soda moves up the straw and onto our tongue as long as we maintain the vacuum.

In the lift pump, the downstroke of the pump handle causes the piston to rise, creating the partial vacuum in the cylinder below the piston. The partial vacuum sucks a column of water up the well pipe and into the cylinder chamber in which the piston operates. At the bottom of this chamber is a flap valve. The column of water rising from the well lifts the flap to enter the chamber. But on a downstroke of the piston, the pressure forces this flap to close and opens a flap

THE LIFT PUMP

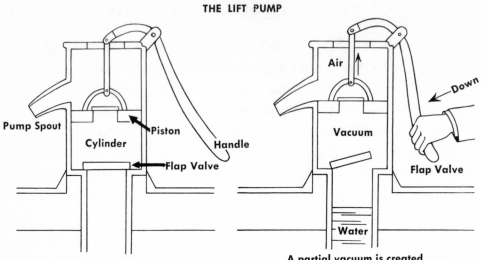

A partial vacuum is created.

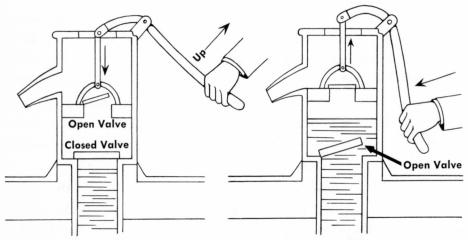

The vacuum causes the water to rise in the well pipe and into cylinder chamber.

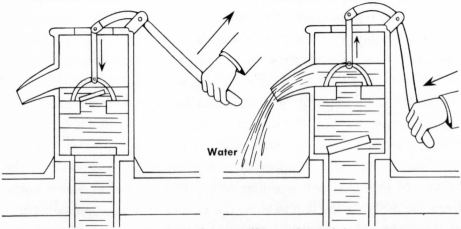

The water, under compression, forces itself up and out of the pump spout.

valve in the piston. The water, under compression, forces its way through the flap valve and out the spout of the pump.

The power of a vacuum will seem amazing indeed when it is remembered that many wells are more than 200 feet deep, and that a small boy can pump water this distance!

The lift pump is the simplest kind of pump. One that is more complicated, and at the same time more efficient, is the *force pump*. It can pump water to higher levels and with greater force than a lift pump, because the force on the downward stroke of the piston is applied to the water as it leaves the pump. It starts its operation in the same way as the lift pump — when the piston moves up it creates a partial vacuum which draws water up into the pump chamber. On the downstroke of the piston, a valve closes and the water is under pressure. But instead of being forced directly out of the pump spout it goes first to an air chamber. The water forced into the air chamber compresses the air at the top, and the force of the compressed air drives the water to its outlet in a steady flow. The lift pump, on the other hand, delivers a pulsating flow of water which stops the moment pumping is stopped.

Improvements on the lift pump and the force pump were not made during the Middle Ages. But once the principle of creating force with the aid of a vacuum was understood, it was not too difficult to develop the kinds of pumps used today on big engineering projects. One of these modern pumps, used in city waterworks, irrigation, dredging, sewage disposal, and mining, is the centrifugal pump. It makes use of both a vacuum and *centrifugal force*.

You can demonstrate centrifugal force in your own kitchen with a marble and a deep mixing bowl. You know, without trying, that if you place the marble anywhere on the inside of the bowl higher than its bottom, gravity will pull it down to the bottom of the bowl. But if you take the bowl in your hands and rotate it in an even circle, slowly at first, then faster and faster, the marble will whirl about the bowl and start to climb the sides as it circles. With a little

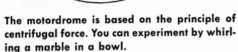
The motordrome is based on the principle of centrifugal force. You can experiment by whirling a marble in a bowl.

practice, you can keep the marble whirling around the top of the bowl at the very edge. Of course, if you whirl it too hard, the marble will fly out across the room. The force that is holding the marble against the upper sides of the bowl, in apparent defiance of the law of gravity, is centrifugal force.

Perhaps you have been to a motordrome at a fair or carnival and marveled at the way daring motorcycle riders climbed the walls of a wooden bowl and whirled around the sides at top speed. This is a dangerous performance, but not nearly as dangerous as it seems, because centrifugal force is holding the motorcycles against the steep sides of the track, just as it did your marble in the bowl. To an experienced rider, there is no more danger in this stunt than there is in riding the motorcycle along a stretch of level highway, so long as the speed is not increased to the point where the rider would whirl his cycle over the edge of the "bowl." The same principle is utilized on the banked turns of a race course. The banking permits race cars to take turns at speeds which would whirl them into skids if the turns were level.

What has all this to do with pumps? The energy developed in centrifugal force can be applied to water as well as other matter. For instance, you can learn to whirl a bucket of water around your head without spilling a drop (better go outside to try this experiment).

The water does not spill because it is pushed against the bottom of the pail by centrifugal force.

If you don't whirl the bucket correctly, the water will fly out with great force. This is the principle used in the centrifugal pump, which operates in the manner here illustrated.

Instead of pails, the centrifugal pump has whirling scoops, each of which drives water out of the chamber and at the same time creates a partial vacuum. This vacuum draws in new water to replace that which is being forced to the pump outlet.

This, then, was the achievement of the Middle Ages — man harnessed the natural forces of nature—wind and water—and made them work for him. The machines by which this was done proved important for the next advance in engineering—the development of man-made sources of power. How that came about during the Industrial Revolution will be discussed in the next chapter.

HOW A CENTRIFUGAL PUMP WORKS

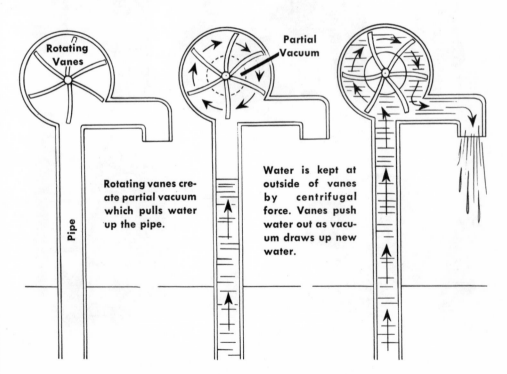

Rotating Vanes

Partial Vacuum

Pipe

Rotating vanes create partial vacuum which pulls water up the pipe.

Water is kept at outside of vanes by centrifugal force. Vanes push water out as vacuum draws up new water.

CHAPTER FIVE

FROM THE INDUSTRIAL REVOLUTION TO THE ATOMIC AGE

THE pump was the most important engineering development of the Middle Ages, and the pump was to become the starting point for the steam engine and all that followed in that remarkable period in man's history we call the Industrial Revolution.

That steam was a hot and violent gas—the result of boiling water —was known to man for thousands of years. That steam had the power to move light objects in its path was also known. There are records of water being boiled (during the Middle Ages) in copper pots so that the steam coming from their spouts would strike the cloth sails of a small windmill attached to a spit in the fireplace. The sails, moved around by the steam, automatically turned the meat that was cooking on the spit. This was certainly, in itself, a kind of crude steam engine.

The thinkers of ancient times speculated on the power available in steam, and some crude steam engines may actually have been built in Greece before 200 B. C. There are writings of a piston and cylinder moved by steam in an invention of Ctesibius, and a drawing of a steam engine by Hero. But we do not know for certain whether any such engines actually were made.

We do know that after centuries of speculation about steam power, one man finally invented a practical steam pump in 1698. He was Thomas Savery, an English mining engineer. In 1702, four years after describing and patenting his idea, Savery set up the world's first steam-engine factory in London.

Savery's engine was a pump, with no cylinder, piston, or other working parts we have come to associate with a steam engine. It worked in two stages. The first stage made use of the fact that steam condenses (that is, shrinks in volume, taking less space) when it is

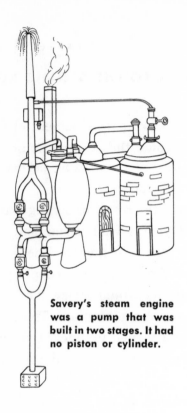

Savery's steam engine was a pump that was built in two stages. It had no piston or cylinder.

cooled suddenly. When steam was condensed in a chamber, it took up less space in the chamber and created a partial vacuum. Savery used this vacuum, in the first stage of his engine, to draw water from a lower level up into the chamber in which he condensed the steam. Then, in the second stage, he raised the water still higher by introducing a new supply of steam into the chamber. By turning valves by hand at regular intervals, Savery and his mechanics could alternate these stages about five times a minute. This produced a constant flow of water. Savery's pumps were created for use in England's mines which were constantly being flooded with water at a rate beyond the capacity of ordinary pumps.

Savery's engine was crude, inefficient and clumsy. A man had to stand by it constantly during its operation, opening and closing valves in just the right rhythm. It was more powerful than the lift pump, but it lacked certain mechanical efficiencies of the lift pump, with its piston and cylinder.

The idea of putting the two mechanisms together, as so often occurs in great engineering advances, belongs to another man. Thomas Newcomen, an English ironworker, borrowed the brick furnaces and copper kettles of the beer-brewing trade in building his engine. With these he created a supply of steam for the same kind of cylinder and piston that had been used for lifting water in the Middle Ages. When the steam entered the cylinder, a spray of cold water condensed it. A vacuum was thus created on the underside of the piston, and the atmospheric pressure on the other side of the piston forced the piston down. The piston rod was connected by a chain to one end of a huge wooden framework, balanced on a central pivot, called a *working beam*. A heavy weight was attached to the other end of the working beam. After the downward stroke of the piston, the vacuum was broken by introducing new steam into the cylinder. The weight on

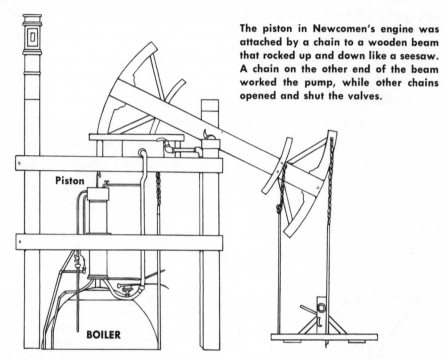

The piston in Newcomen's engine was attached by a chain to a wooden beam that rocked up and down like a seesaw. A chain on the other end of the beam worked the pump, while other chains opened and shut the valves.

Piston

BOILER

the beam then pulled the piston up. Another spray of water condensed the steam again, and the piston was pulled down again to start another cycle.

Newcomen's working beam was primarily a huge lever balanced on a fulcrum. On one side, the lever was forced down by a weight, and on the other side it was pulled down by the pressure created when a vacuum was produced.

Notice the curved arms at the ends of the working beam. The arms were curved in order that the chain could be taken up as the end of the working beam rose; this curvature also insured that the piston rod would not be bent or forced out of line from the cylinder.

If the ends of the beam had not been curved, the piston rods and pump rods would have been bent every time the beam rocked up and down, since the beam end would be describing an arc—the very arc in fact, that the ends are curved to eliminate.

Newcomen's engines were crude and inefficient—but they were good enough to be used, in every mine shaft in England and on the European continent, as fast as they could be turned out. The working beam was good only for pumping. But the machine was the best means devised up to that time for keeping the mines clear of water.

Newcomen designed his valves so that they opened and closed automatically with the rocking motion of the beam, admitting steam to the cylinder and then water to condense the steam. The fitting of piston and cylinder in these engines was very crude. Machines with pistons that were smooth working, yet steamtight and watertight, did not as yet exist. Newcomen made his pistons slightly smaller than the cylinder, then put a leather washer at the end of the cylinder to insure a snug fit.

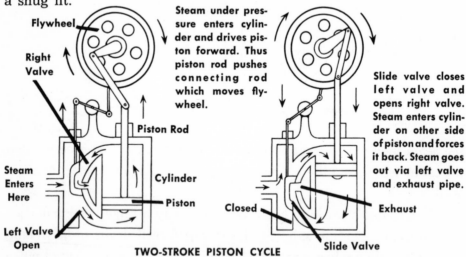

TWO-STROKE PISTON CYCLE

Although Newcomen's engine certainly made use of steam, it used it only to obtain a vacuum when that steam was condensed inside the cylinder. For, remember, the piston moved when it was pushed by the *atmosphere* on the other side of the piston outside of the cylinder, where no vacuum existed. Newcomen's engine made no use at all of the biggest energy potential in steam—its *expansive* force.

James Watt was the first engine-builder to think about making use of the expansive force of steam. But he did not actually do this with the engines he built. Watt first improved on the design of the Newcomen engine. As a mechanical engineer in Glasgow, Watt was called on to make repairs on a Newcomen engine. It struck him that the engine wasted fuel and heat because the walls of the cylinder had to be heated and cooled with each cycle of the engine.

Watt provided a separate chamber in which the steam could be cooled and condensed. He kept the cylinder piston hot at all times by putting an outer covering, or jacket, around the cylinder, and filling the jacket with surplus steam. This improvement was a great success, since Watt's engine operated by using approximately ¼ of the coal the Newcomen engine had required.

Watt invented his separate condenser in 1765. He followed this with other improvements on the Newcomen steam engine, and by 1769 he had changed it in so many ways that he was able to obtain a patent for his own steam engine. The Watt engine was double-acting —it applied steam and vacuum to both sides of the piston as it went back and forth in the cylinder.

Although Watt, in applying for his patent, indicated that he wanted to make use of the expansive force of steam, he never did so. He was aware of the power of steam under pressure, but he was fearful of explosions.

It was an American, Oliver Evans, who first dared to make an engine using steam under high pressure. In 1787 the state of Pennsylvania granted him patent rights to a steam engine for grinding flour, but ignored his request for rights to a "steam wagon" that he hoped to build as the first self-propelled vehicle. Evans' steam engine eliminated the condenser, and the steam was heated to a pressure of 50 pounds per square inch, the first time that steam for such an engine had been brought to higher than atmospheric pressure.

This was the dawn of the Industrial Revolution. Thereafter, improvements in the efficiency of the steam engine and the uses to which

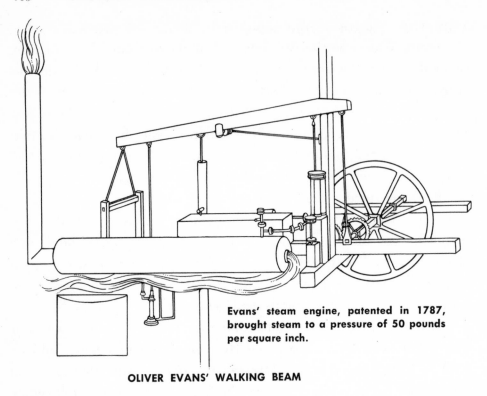

Evans' steam engine, patented in 1787, brought steam to a pressure of 50 pounds per square inch.

OLIVER EVANS' WALKING BEAM

these engines were put increased rapidly. Steam engines were harnessed to belts and pulleys, and to gears and crankshafts. They were used to operate all kinds of machinery. They were put on rails to pull trains, they were put into ships (soon eliminating sailing vessels for all commercial purposes). They were used in the first automobiles, and it has been only a little more than 30 years since the last steam automobile was manufactured in the United States. Modern steam engines, and especially the steam turbine, are still important in the field of mechanical engineering.

The importance of the steam engine was well recognized in the time of Newcomen and Watt. For the first time in history, a source of power which did not depend on animals, on wind, or on the supply of falling or running water, had been made available. Here was a machine that could be set up anywhere, and could run night and day as long as it was fed the necessary wood or coal.

But the Industrial Revolution was accompanied by many other

developments important to engineering besides the steam engine. This was a period of great inventive activity, for the world was changing. The hand labor of the feudal system was giving way to a system of free enterprise and machine-made manufacturing on a massive scale. This new system required that a great many things be produced in numbers which had never been produced before.

NEW MEASUREMENTS AND FORMULAS

New ways of measuring and testing the strength of materials were required in the new scheme of things. The steam engine, for instance, brought in a new measurement—the measurement of power that we use today under the odd name, *horsepower*.

The men who developed the first steam engines had to explain to the mine owners (to whom they wanted to sell their engines) just what the new pumping machinery could do. The only term the mine owners could understand was one that would compare the work of the steam engine with the strength of the teams of horses that worked the old-fashioned mine pumps. The steam-engine men first pointed out that their engines could do the work of the horses used in any given operation. They also explained that since the engine could work as long it was supplied fuel, it would replace all the teams of horses used in relays as one team grew tired.

It was James Watt who first conducted experiments with brewery horses to find out exactly how much work they could do. He estimated from these tests that a strong work horse was able to lift 32,400 foot-pounds per minute. This figure was rounded off to 33,000 foot-pounds per minute. And that is what we mean by horsepower today. A one-horsepower motor is capable of doing work equal to lifting 33,000 pounds to a height of one foot in one minute.

This does not mean that you could tie a rope to a 33,000-pound weight and lift it one foot into the air with a one-horsepower electric motor. Because of the inertia of the weight and the lack of leverage, the little motor would simply stall, or if not turned off, would burn out its bearings or be pulled apart under the strain. Under the proper mechanical conditions, however, any one-horsepower motor, if properly geared, could perform exactly this task in one minute.

The Industrial Revolution brought another new idea to engineering. Men began testing materials to see if they were strong enough for the engine, building, bridge, or other project planned. Before this, they had been satisfied to guess at the kind and amount of material that would be required for a particular job. After a number of Roman buildings had collapsed after their erection, for example, Roman engineers overbuilt everything — that is, they made everything a lot stronger than it needed to be, and they used a great deal more material than was necessary. But in the later age of the Industrial Revolution, time, labor and materials had become increasingly more expensive. Slave labor (which did not have to be paid, of course) was not available, as it had been for the Romans. Engineering projects were getting so big that the amount of required material became an important factor, and projects often had to be completed much more quickly than had been the case in the ancient world where a number of engineering wonders took several generations to complete.

The first machines to test materials, such as iron rods, stone blocks and lumber, were put together at the University of Leyden by a professor named Pieter van Musschenbroek, in 1729. He tested these materials for their reaction to tension (being pulled apart), compression (being pushed together), and bending. This was followed, in 1768, by a bigger and more practical machine built by the French engineer, Jean Rodolphe Perronet. Perronet had drawn the plans for a bridge at Neuilly, France. He wanted to know whether the flat arches he had designed would bear the weight of the bridge span.

These early tests of materials are seldom mentioned in textbooks. But they were very important in the history of engineering. Because of them engineers could build safely, and yet not be forced to overbuild or to use too many materials.

Modern engineering materials are tested by much more elaborate methods, so that what the engineer calls the "margin of safety" can be established for every part of a project. This does not mean that human errors do not occur even today. Buildings and bridges still collapse, although designed and erected by the most skilled architects and engineers. Airplanes still crash without any reasonable explanation, disaster-proof ships still sink, and other accidents occur in the best-laid engineering plans. But now these disasters are known to be due to human errors made in calculations, and not to a lack of information about the materials being used. Today engineers do not put new materials into use until they know all about their reactions to stress, strain, heat, cold, fatigue and many other things.

When you go to a movie today, you are entirely safe if a fire breaks out in the projection booth where the movie projector is located. That is because the projection booth is like a fireproof box. The only openings are the door through which the operator comes and goes, and one small window through which the movie film is projected onto the big screen over the heads of the audience. The door is shut at all times during a performance, and the small window has a sliding panel which is held up by a chain. One link of this chain is made of a mixture (or alloy) of lead, tin and other metals which have a low melting point. Should a fire break out in the projection room, the heat melts the soft link in the chain, and the sliding panel drops, sealing off the projection booth from the rest of the theater. Since air is shut off from the booth, a fire quickly dies down, even though the film is highly inflammable.

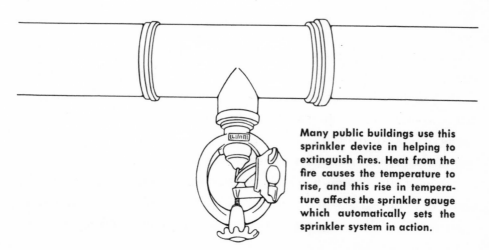

Many public buildings use this sprinkler device in helping to extinguish fires. Heat from the fire causes the temperature to rise, and this rise in temperature affects the sprinkler gauge which automatically sets the sprinkler system in action.

Modern fire protection systems use this property of low melting points. Chemicals which can smother fires are placed in pipes running along the ceiling of a room. Sprinkler heads are placed at intervals along these pipes. The sprinkler heads are capped with metal of a low melting point. When a fire breaks out anywhere in the room, the temperature rises to a point which melts the metal caps over the sprinkler heads, and the fire-extinguishing chemical is sprayed over the blaze.

This principle of melting points was known to the steam-engine builders of the Industrial Revolution. After a number of steam boilers had burned out because the water had boiled away, it was discovered that a plug of soft metal could be used which would melt and release a warning jet of steam before any real damage to the boiler could occur. To avoid boiler explosions, they designed the safety valve, which was a weighted valve, loosely fitted, which lifted up to allow steam to

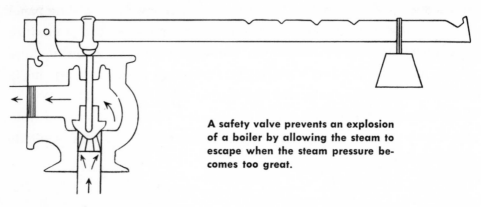

A safety valve prevents an explosion of a boiler by allowing the steam to escape when the steam pressure becomes too great.

escape when the pressure became too great. If your mother has a pressure cooker, you will notice a little valve popping up and down on the lid. This is a safety valve, which keeps steam from building up in the cooker to the point where it would explode and send your dinner flying all over the kitchen.

As engineers worked to perfect the steam engine, they had to make closer fits of such working parts as the piston and cylinder. The whole system of measurements was expanded. Where one-sixteenth of an inch had been a pretty precise measurement, machining now required first hundredths of an inch, and then *thousandths* of an inch as workable fractions. In many countries, the decimal system, or systems of tens, was used because in engineering work it was simpler and more precise. Elaborate formulas and tables came into use, and the engineer's slide rule for making quick computations came into being. With a slide rule an engineer can instantly find the square of a number or the area of a circle. To perform these chores arithmetically on paper might require hours of work on certain projects.

Growing out of Galileo's famous experiments in measuring small intervals of time, a whole new system of mathematics, including modern algebra, geometry, and calculus, was given to the engineer as a tool. Galileo's experiments with falling weights established the fact that heavier weights fell to earth at the same rate of speed as lighter ones. Before 1583, when Galileo began his experiments, everyone had assumed that a heavier weight would fall faster. Galileo then applied his experiments to swinging pendulums, and found that the weight of the pendulum had no effect on the time of its swing. Instead, he found that the time it takes a pendulum to complete its swing depends only on the length of the pendulum.

Galileo's experiments with the pendulum not only led to the development of pendulum clocks and other timing devices—they also made possible new developments in military engineering.

Gunpowder had been known to the ancient Chinese empires, and

Castle walls were no obstacles to an enemy after the invention of gunpowder.

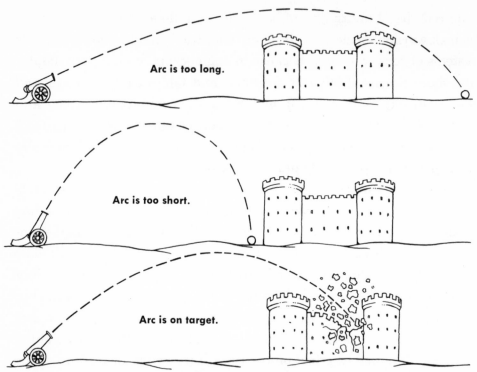

The cannon's mouth had to be placed at just the right angle in order for the cannonball to hit its target.

in Medieval Europe some use had been made of it as an explosive in breaking loose rocks and ores in quarries and mines. But it was not until 1343 that gunpowder came into wide use as a charge for firing pistols, muskets and cannon. Galileo's experiments had shown that gravity played a part in describing the arc made by a weighted pendulum. The same principle could be applied (sort of upside down) to describe the arc made by a cannonball. By working out the pull of gravity on a cannonball as it left the muzzle of a gun, it was possible to predict where the ball would strike as the cannon's mouth was pointed at different angles.

Gunpowder and guns changed the whole way of life of the peoples of Europe. No longer could the common people look to the castles of feudal lords for protection against their country's enemies—cannon shells easily knocked down the stone walls of castles. The armor the knights wore into battle could not protect them against the impact of bullets, and their companies of archers could be outshot by companies of men with muskets.

Marine engineering also benefited from the new mathematics founded on Galileo's discoveries and improved by the mathematicians who continued his basic work. Navigation instruments, such as the sextant, enabled the masters of sailing vessels to tell exactly where they were at any moment during a voyage.

Galileo's and Sir Isaac Newton's experiments with gravity led directly to the establishment of many fundamental principles of mechanical and structural engineering. Let us examine one of them— the cantilever principle of construction.

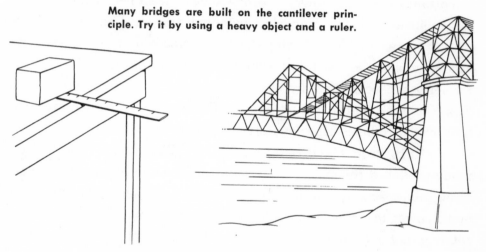

Many bridges are built on the cantilever principle. Try it by using a heavy object and a ruler.

You can demonstrate the cantilever principle, by which many bridges are designed, right at your desk or worktable. All you need is a ruler and some object heavy enough to hold an inch or two of the ruler to the edge of the table while the rest of the ruler projects over space. This is the principle which allows bridges to be built over rivers and canyons without any supporting piers.

DEVELOPMENT OF MACHINE TOOLS

The steam engine could not have been improved much beyond the point reached by the first engines built by Newcomen and Watt had it not been for the development of power-operated machine tools.

Typical of the way engineers borrowed from each other to solve problems was the instance in which John Wilkinson used steam power to make a machine whose purpose was to improve the steam engine itself. Wilkinson's machine was the first boring mill, cutting true round holes through metal bars to form the cylinders in which the steam-engine pistons worked back and forth. With smooth, true cylinders to which to fit their pistons, the steam-engine builders could avoid the breakdowns which occurred when pistons jammed. They could also avoid the loss of efficiency involved when steam leaked through ill-fitting piston-cylinder fittings.

A lathe that would cut threaded screws and bolts was the next important step in machinery to prove to be of great benefit to mechanical engineers. Henry Maudsley patented this in London in 1800.

A planer that could trim the flat surfaces of metal parts with accuracy was the next big step in power machinery. Work that formerly had been done by painstaking labor with hand chisels and files was done with a few strokes of the big power planer invented by Richard Roberts of Manchester, England, in 1817.

In 1818, from the inventive genius of Eli Whitney, who had already produced the cotton gin and introduced the principle of interchangeable parts in manufacture, came the next and most important of all power machinery inventions—the milling machine. This was a rotating tool with many cutting edges. In one cutting operation it was able to make many duplicate metal parts. There are mechanical engineers who say that the milling machine is man's most important invention, because without it we could not perform the miracles of mass production that characterize our age.

Next, in 1840, came James Nasmyth's drill press, able to drill holes at any desired angle or depth, and automatically controlled for precision within the closest measurements.

With these and other machines developed during the early days of the Industrial Revolution, the shaping and finishing of metal was made almost as easy as the shaping of wood or clay. Metal parts could take any shape and measurement the designer called for, and the

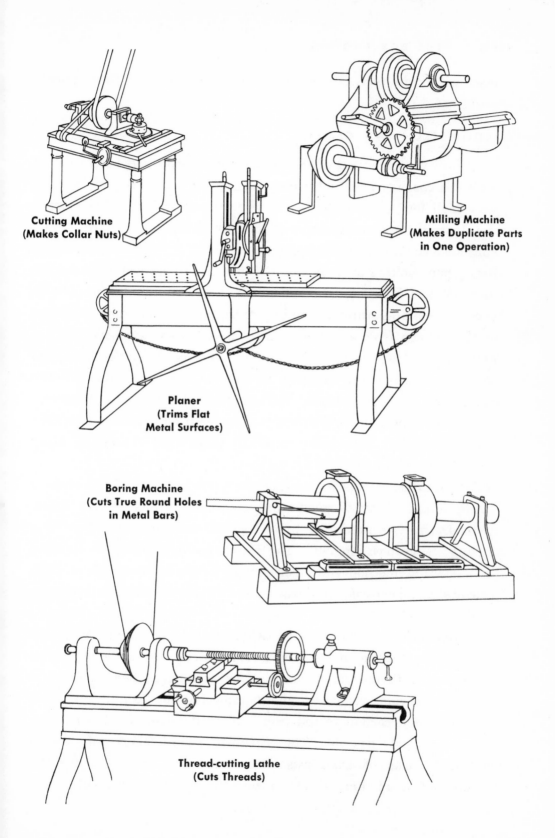

Cutting Machine
(Makes Collar Nuts)

Milling Machine
(Makes Duplicate Parts
in One Operation)

Planer
(Trims Flat
Metal Surfaces)

Boring Machine
(Cuts True Round Holes
in Metal Bars)

Thread-cutting Lathe
(Cuts Threads)

machines could turn out as many identical parts as the engineers could use.

IRON, STEEL AND CEMENT

Until the invention of the steam engine, iron had been smelted with charcoal used as fuel. Charcoal is made by heating wood to a very high temperature, but so slowly that the wood never catches fire. Instead the wood changes chemically to the black, hard, brittle substance you are probably most familiar with as the fuel your family uses when cooking over an outdoor grill. Charcoal was used by the first smelters because, while it burns slowly, it can be brought to very high temperatures by adding extra oxygen, as when a stream of air is blown from a bellows. But charcoal is an expensive fuel for any industrial use such as the smelting of iron. After the Industrial Revolution, when iron began to be used in large quantities for the making of engines, bridges, and some buildings, charcoal became even more expensive, and so much of it was used in ironmaking that England's forests were being ruined. It takes a lot of wood to make only a little charcoal.

It was of enormous importance, therefore, when in 1709 Abraham Darby found a way to smelt iron using coal as fuel. Within a few years Darby was producing more than 50 tons of iron a year in a factory in western England. The Darby family handed down their iron-smelting method from generation to generation, and in 1775 Darby's grandson cast the beams and ribs for the world's first iron bridge.

Ironworkers of the ancient world and of the Middle Ages had made steel. But they made it by a very difficult process, heating iron in contact with powdered charcoal for as long as two weeks, and then hammering, reheating and hammering the iron again. This process added carbon to the iron, and made steel which was very hard and yet flexible. The Spanish swordmakers of Toledo and the Turks of Damascus made very fine steel, as did the makers of steel knives and razors in Sheffield, England. But only a small amount of steel could be made this way. And, while steel was known to be stronger and more satisfactory in many ways than iron, it was too expensive and too much trouble to make for large engineering projects.

Curiously, the development of a steelmaking process suitable for industry grew out of an Englishman's endeavor to improve cannon shells. The man was Henry Bessemer, and during the Crimean War he invented a bullet-shaped cannon charge to replace the round cannon balls that had been used. Bessemer's shell spiraled as it left the cannon's mouth, and this motion steadied its flight and made possible more accurate shooting than was possible with round cannon balls. However, Bessemer's shell required a much larger charge of powder. So great was the charge that there was constant danger of exploding the cast-iron cannon, and of killing or injuring members of the gun crew.

Bessemer saw that he must develop a stronger metal for cannon if his artillery shell was to be used. Bessemer remembered that he

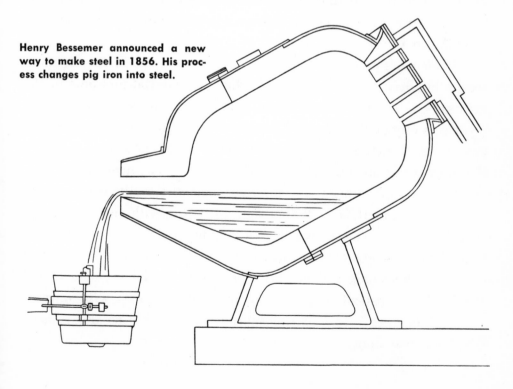

Henry Bessemer announced a new way to make steel in 1856. His process changes pig iron into steel.

had seen a remarkable change in the composition of the outside of a molten mass of pig iron, and thought perhaps the change he had seen was the result of part of the mass being exposed to a current of air. He experimented with this idea, and succeeded in making a rather poor, soft grade of steel by melting pig iron in a cylinder, or crucible, and then blowing jets of air through the mass of molten metal. The air forced the melted metal to oxidize, or burn partially, and took most of the carbon out of the iron along with the impurities.

Bessemer's steel was poor because it was impossible to tell how much of the carbon would be removed. Steel containing too little carbon would be too soft. But Bessemer's process, announced in 1856, was almost immediately improved upon by a fellow expert in metals, Robert Forester Mushet. Mushet added a quantity of *spiegeleisen,* an iron ore containing a high percentage of manganese, to the melted metal, just after the jets of air had been forced through the mass. This exhausted the oxygen in the mass, and put back a certain amount of carbon to replace that which had been oxidized in the smelting. The result was a hard, strong, high-carbon steel which made excellent machine tools.

Bessemer's process, as improved by Mushet, was in use for more than a hundred years and supplied the raw material for some of the greatest engineering projects the world has ever seen. Today the process is outdated, and more complicated but much better methods are in use. Bessemer's contribution to the world, however, is one of the most important milestones in the history of engineering.

A milestone almost as important was the rediscovery of the working of cement, a skill that had been lost with the fall of the Roman Empire. The knowledge of making pozzuolana, which the Roman builders had compounded of the fine ash from volcanoes and powdered limestone, had not been passed on to the builders of the Middle Ages. Instead of joining their building stones with mortar, medievel engineers had used iron rods and hooks, as the ancient Egyptians had done.

Something like Roman cement was developed in 1756 by John Smeaton, builder of the Eddystone lighthouse off the coast of England. Smeaton had experimented with many materials in search of something that would harden under water and thus serve as a base for his lighthouse. He found that lime containing clay worked best as a mortar which would harden under water and resist deterioration. Builders then looked everywhere for natural cement, and in certain locations found just the right mixture of limestone and clay. This was roasted and ground to a fine powder, and was called natural cement, or hydraulic cement.

The Portland cement we use today was invented in 1824 by Joseph Aspdin of Leeds, England. He found he could make a better cement than that found in nature by mixing, powdering, roasting and grinding together a carefully measured mixture of limestone and clay which contained a precise proportion of the ores called silica and alumina.

Cement is only the first step toward making concrete. Concrete is a mixture of cement, sand, gravel and water. The proportions in which these are used are called the *mix*, and the proportions vary according to whether a mighty dam, a concrete driveway, or a flower box is to be built. A standard mix for most household cement projects is the 1:2:3 mix, which means one part of Portland cement, two parts of fine sand and three parts of clean, small-stoned gravel. Water is mixed in with the three dry ingredients until a stiff, smooth *grout*, like a cake batter, results. An exact amount of water cannot be specified for the grout, since the other ingredients, especially the sand, contain water themselves, which varies according to weather conditions. If the sand is especially moist, the grout will require less water than it will if the sand is very dry.

Concrete hardens within a few hours after being poured into the shape it is to take. But it is not then ready for use. It must be "cured" — that is, it must be kept covered and wet for from 10 days to two weeks. If this curing is not observed, concrete will crack and crumble within a short time. If properly cured, however, concrete is almost as strong as natural stone, and much more resistant to water.

No one knows exactly what happens inside the concrete during this curing process, except that some chemical change takes place which hardens the concrete.

It's easy to mix a small quantity of concrete. Perhaps you would like to make a flower box like the one shown in the drawing on the opposite page. If you are handy with tools, you can easily make the two wooden forms needed to shape and hold the concrete until it is set. The larger form is a box with no top, and is made of five pieces of wood cut to the dimensions shown. The smaller, inner form which shapes the inside of the flower box is made of four pieces of wood, plus the two strips which lay across the outer form and hold the inner form in place.

With the forms built, you are ready to mix concrete. You'll need a bag of cement, enough sand to equal two bags of cement in volume, and a quantity of gravel equal to three bags of cement. A bag of cement contains one cubic foot. You can make a rough measuring box with five pieces of board one foot square. Filled with sand or gravel, it will make one cubic foot of these ingredients. Fill it with sand twice, and with gravel three times.

You can mix these ingredients together with a shovel, a hoe, or a rake. Mix them thoroughly, then make a hole in the center of the pile. Pour a little water in the hole, and mix it thoroughly with the dry ingredients. It will take about five gallons of water, but the water should be added slowly and you should stop short of the full five gallons if the mixture starts to get runny. A good mixture should run, but will sort of "plop" off the end of your shovel or hoe.

You must be sure to mix your concrete when the temperature is above freezing. The chemical curing process will not take place if the temperature is at freezing or below.

The two parts of your form should be greased or oiled so the cement will not stick to them. Then the inner form is placed inside the large form and the concrete is poured into the space between the

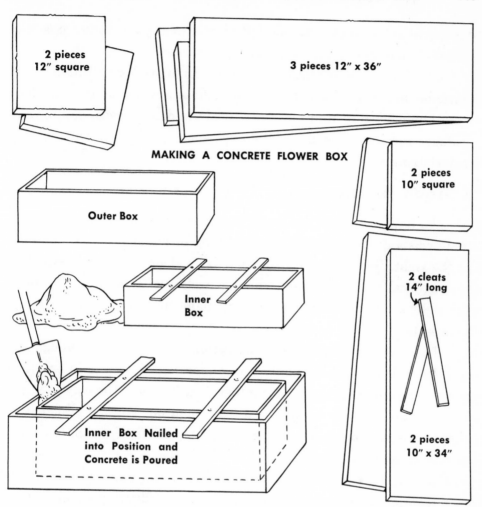

2 pieces 12" square

3 pieces 12" x 36"

MAKING A CONCRETE FLOWER BOX

2 pieces 10" square

Outer Box

Inner Box

2 cleats 14" long

Inner Box Nailed into Position and Concrete is Poured

2 pieces 10" x 34"

edges. The bottom of your flower box should be poured carefully and smoothed down for a nice flat bottom. A round wooden plug should be pushed through the bottom before the cement dries. This will form a hole through which water can drain when flowers are planted in the dirt-filled box.

When the concrete has set—that is, become hardened—you can pull out the inner form and pry off the sides and bottom of the outer form. There is your concrete flower box. But it's not finished yet— remember that concrete has to be cured. You do this by covering the flower box with a piece of burlap, pressing it well down inside the flower box. Sprinkle this burlap with a hose, and wet it down every day for about a week. At the end of this time your flower box will be cured, and should last for a long, long time.

Concrete gave the builders of the Industrial Revolution a remarkable material which they could mold to any shape desired. Concrete found its way into buildings, bridges, dams, roads, sewers and drainage systems. It is one of the engineer's most important building materials today.

A FLOOD OF INVENTIONS AND DISCOVERIES

We have seen that not many steam engines could be made until there was a good supply of the right kind of metal for parts. Enough of the right kind of metal could not be had until a new method of making steel was found, and enough parts could not be made until the right kinds of machines were available to cut and shape metal into parts.

The world of engineering was getting complicated, although the Industrial Revolution was only a few years old. Progress in one field often depended on progress in another field. This was the way progress in technology was to be achieved from then on. For the rest of this chapter we shall be able to discuss only very briefly the changes made as one inventor after another filled more than a century and a half with a bewildering number of improvements. Not only did one invention inspire another; new materials, as they developed, also gave opportunities for new inventions.

The different branches of engineering began to take shape as we know them today. But one field borrowed from another so rapidly that we can discuss them sensibly only as part of one big picture. Inventions and discoveries followed each other so rapidly from 1800 to the present day that dates become relatively unimportant in this pageant of technical progress.

The steam engine began as a machine for pumping water from mines. But it was not long before mechanics saw many other uses for the new source of power. Soon, steam engines were digging canals,

Richard Trevithick built a steam carriage that was the forerunner of our modern day automobiles.

sawing lumber and driving piers to support buildings and bridges.

Many men were quick to see that Watt's steam engine could be put on wheels and that it could then propel itself. The idea of running cars over iron rails was not new—horses and mules had been used to pull loaded cars over rails in mines and on hillside quarries for a long time. Richard Trevithick is credited with being the first man to build a successful steam locomotive, in 1804. At the same time, Trevithick built a passenger-carrying steam carriage, the ancestor of the modern automobile.

If a steam engine could run over roads and pull cars over rails, there was at least one man who believed it could just as well push a boat through water. He was Robert Fulton, and he proved his point in 1807. By 1821 the first iron-hulled passenger steamship had been built, and a side-wheeled steamer had been used in battle as a warship. In 1849, steam was put to work drilling through rock.

Eli Whitney had laid the foundation for modern mass-production methods during the Revolutionary War by producing identical musket parts so that any of the full number of interchangeable parts could be assembled into a shooting weapon. Before that, each musket had been built individually, part by part, and none of its parts would exactly fit another musket, except by accident. Jethro Wood's iron plow (1819) was among the first of many modern farm tools and machines which were to increase production and make the farmer's work easier.

THE WORLD OF ELECTRICITY

As the engineers struggled to perfect steam power, another group of experimenters were developing what was to be an even more important power source—electricity. Static electricity—the kind of an electrical charge created when you rub a piece of amber and find that it is able to pick up feathers, lint, or small bits of paper—had been known before the time of Christ.

Glass and hard rubber are modern substances which behave the same way as amber when rubbed briskly on woolen cloth. You can discover this for yourself by rubbing a glass rod against your clothing (if woolen), and then picking up scraps of paper with the tip of the rod. The ancient experimenters had no reasonable explanation for what we know as static electricity. There were some further experiments with static electricity during the Middle Ages. A few more substances were found which had this strange power to attract light objects. But it was a feeble source of power and attracted little serious attention until 1749, when America's Benjamin Franklin proved, with his famous kite experiment, that static electricity generated in a thunderstorm could be conducted down a kite string to the earth. The lightning arrester, a valuable thing in itself, came out of these experiments, but electricity still was not recognized as a possible source of power.

Luigi Galvani, a scientist at the University of Bologna, in Italy, performed an experiment in 1786 which was important, but which

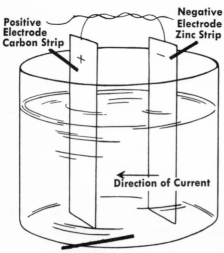

Volta's wet cell changes chemical energy into electrical energy through the chemical action of the diluted sulfuric acid on zinc.

JOSEPH HENRY'S ELECTROMAGNET

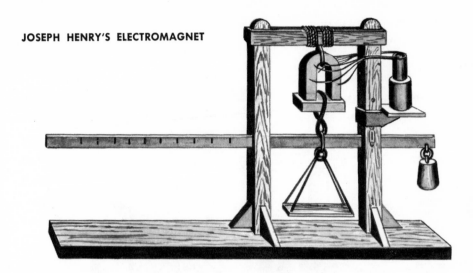

Galvani completely misunderstood. Galvani attached the legs of a freshly killed frog to a copper hook and hung the hook over an iron railing. The frog legs danced violently when the two metals touched. Galvani thought this proved that a frog's legs contained electricity! Not until 14 years later (1800) did another Italian scientist, Count Alessandro Volta, discover the truth of the matter. He established that it was the contact of two unlike metals—copper and iron—which gave off the electrical current, and the frog's legs merely conducted this current from one metal to another. Volta showed that he could produce an electrical charge by putting copper and zinc plates in contact. He touched one end of each plate to paper moistened with salt water, and touched together the opposite ends of the plates. He made this into a crude sort of a battery, called a voltaic cell.

Such batteries were good only for laboratory experiments. But with one of them, a relationship between electricity and magnetism was discovered. Hans Christian Oersted, a professor at the University of Copenhagen, was sending current through a wire when he noticed that the electrical current was affecting a compass in the room. Oersted discovered that every conductor of electricity sets up a magnetic field about itself while current is passing through.

Oersted made this discovery in 1820, but since the magnetic field around a single wire was weak, there was no practical use for his finding. In 1830, however, Joseph Henry discovered that the magnetic

FARADAY'S DYNAMO

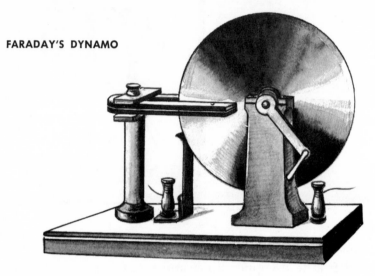

field around a wire carrying current would become much stronger if the wire were wound into a coil. He thus made the first *electromagnet* —a highly practical discovery. Electromagnets have hundreds of uses in all fields of engineering. Small electromagnets are found in telephones and in household doorbells. Large electromagnets pick up tons of iron and steel.

The final discoveries which were to open wide the field of electrical engineering were made, at about the same time as Henry's experiments, by Michael Faraday of England. Faraday first discovered that when a coil of wire was set in motion near a magnet, the magnet induced a current of electricity in the wire. This is the way a modern dynamo generates electricity. A coil is revolved inside the field of a large magnet, thus generating electricity. The power that revolves the coil may come from water power, or from a steam or gasoline engine. But it is the whirling of the huge coil of wire inside the field of a huge magnet which generates electricity.

The electric motor was the result of Faraday's second great discovery. He found that if a current is sent through a coil of wire suspended between the poles of a magnet, the coil of wire will rotate.

With Faraday's two discoveries, man had two keys to electricity —he knew how to create it, and how to put its energy to useful work.

In physical appearance, there is not too much difference between a dynamo and an electric motor. The difference is in purpose. The dynamo uses motion in a magnetic field to produce electric current. The electric motor uses electric current to produce motion. To do this, the electric motor uses the opposite poles of the magnetic field to alternately attract and repel the armature of a rotor, as in the simplified drawing of an electric motor on this page. (The armature is simply a more efficient version of Faraday's suspended coil of wire.) The attracting and repelling forces make the rotor spin, and the resulting power is transmitted to useful work by means of bearings, pulleys, gears and other simple mechanical devices.

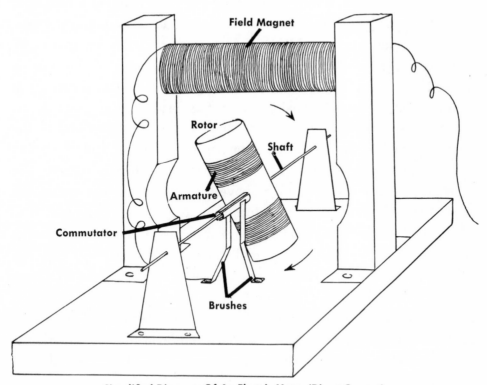

Simplified Diagram Of An Electric Motor (Direct Current)

The basic parts of an electric motor are the armature and shaft, a field magnet, a commutator and the frame which holds these parts in position. The two field poles are connected by a field coil which also makes contact with the commutator. When current enters the field magnet, it makes one pole positive and the other pole negative. The current passes through a carbon brush to the armature. The armature becomes magnetized, and the positive pole of the field magnet attracts the negative pole of the armature. There is a corresponding attraction of unlike poles at the opposite end, and the armature turns on its shaft. The commutator reverses the current in the armature.

When the armature has turned one half of the way around the circumference of the shaft, the poles are alike, and they *repel* each other. Another half of the way around, the poles are attracting each other again. This alternate attraction and repulsion cause the armature to continue to spin smoothly.

The tin-and-nail motor on the opposite page runs on a couple of dry cells or will operate on 6 volts a.c. provided by a transformer. The electromagnets or field coils are wound in series on two nails, both windings being in the same direction. One end of the wire is scraped bare and twisted to form a tight coil which serves as a binding post, it being tacked down to the baseboard at point A. At this point a connection to the current is made. The other end of the wire is tacked to the yoke that supports the upper end of the rotor. Bare copper wire is used as a brush, rubbing lightly against the edges of the rotor about ½ inch above the base. The other end of the brush wire is bared and formed into a binding-post coil at point B to which the other side of the current is connected. Center-punch marks are made in the yoke and in a small tin base plate, halfway between the two nails. Then the rotor is set in place so that the arms are about ⅛ inch above the tops of the nails. The brush is adjusted so that it touches the edges of the rotor and also releases before the arms pass over the nail heads. After connecting the motor to the current supply, give the rotor a start by turning it.

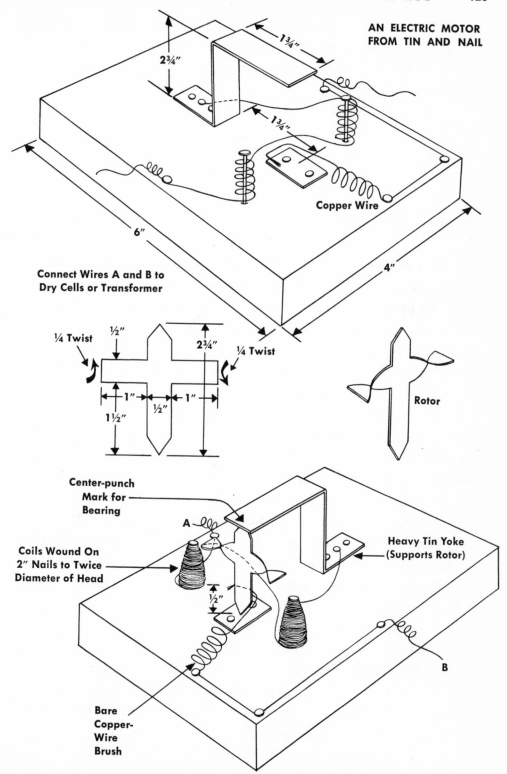

AN ELECTRIC MOTOR
FROM TIN AND NAIL

2¾"

1¾"

1¾"

Copper Wire

6"

4"

Connect Wires A and B to
Dry Cells or Transformer

¼ Twist

½"

2¾"

¼ Twist

1"

1"

½"

1½"

Rotor

Center-punch
Mark for
Bearing

A

Coils Wound On
2" Nails to Twice
Diameter of Head

½"

Heavy Tin Yoke
(Supports Rotor)

B

Bare
Copper-
Wire
Brush

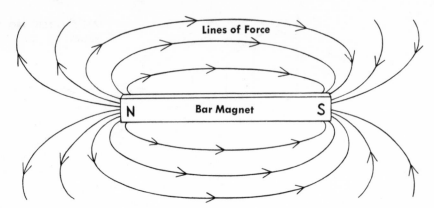

Lines of Force

N   Bar Magnet   S

The greater the strength of the magnet, the greater the strength of the magnetic field.

You will remember that Michael Faraday discovered the principle of the dynamo, or generator, when he found that electric current could be produced in a conductor, such as a copper wire, by moving the conductor in the field of a magnet. Other experimenters found that a current was produced when a magnet was set in motion near a stationary conductor. But the current would flow only when either the magnet or the conductor was in motion.

The region around a magnet where its magnetic influence can be experienced is called the magnetic field. To help us imagine a magnetic field we must think of lines of force passing from the positive pole of a magnet and curving around to the magnet's negative pole.

When a conductor moves across the lines of force in a magnetic field, it "cuts" the lines and induces a current in the conductor. The magnitude of the current induced depends on the speed at which the lines of force are "cut" and the strength of the lines of force.

The forces of attraction and repulsion between like and opposite poles are at work in the generator, just as they are in the electric motor.

The principle is the same as that of the huge electric motors which operate locomotives and elevators in big buildings. Dynamos may also be small, such as the ordinary automobile generator. But the most important generators, which change the water power of giant dams into electrical current, which is then sent to cities hundreds of miles away, are very large.

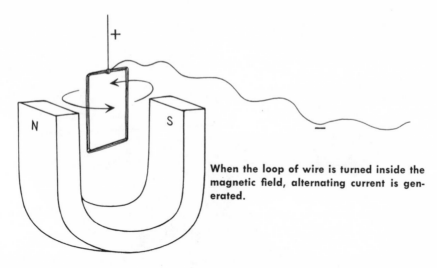

When the loop of wire is turned inside the magnetic field, alternating current is generated.

In the simplest kind of a generator, a loop of wire is turned inside a magnetic field. The two sides of the loop cut through the magnetic lines of force in opposite directions and thus cause a current to flow around the loop in a continuous current. When the loop is halfway around, it will be seen that for an instant no lines of force are being cut, and therefore no current is created for the brief time the loop is in this position. As the loop of wire continues its circuit, however, lines of

This large generator is based on the simple principle demonstrated above.

Nikolaus Otto invented a successful gasoline engine in 1878.

force are again cut, but this time from the opposite direction. The
current, therefore, flows around the loop of wire in the opposite direction. This is alternating current, in contrast to the direct current
supplied by batteries or by certain special kinds of generators. There
are also transformers which change alternating current into direct
current. But 95 percent of the electricity generated in North America
is alternating current.

This, then, is the simplest kind of dynamo, or generator—a loop
of wire revolved in a magnetic field. In large generating stations, of
course, the dynamos are much more complicated. The loop of wire
is replaced by armatures of coiled wire, and the magnetic field is a
series of fields with as many as eight, twelve, or sixteen magnetic
poles. A single generator of the largest type can supply electrical
energy for a city of 500,000 people.

THE GASOLINE ENGINE

Man's search for powerful sources of power did not end with
the invention of the steam engine and the electric motor. Scientists
had long been aware of the explosive power of expanding gases when
they were ignited. During the Middle Ages there were experiments
with gunpowder in the hope that a power engine might result. But

gunpowder proved to be too dangerous and too unpredictable.

Alcohol and crude forms of gasoline were the most promising materials the early experimenters found. When allowed to form vapor, or gas, as they evaporated in air, these materials would explode violently when ignited.

If you pour some alcohol on a flat surface and put a match to it, it will burn; but it will not explode. That is because the alcohol is liquid, and has not had a chance to evaporate and form a gas. If you were to put the same amount of alcohol in a small tin can, hold your hand over the mouth of the can and shake it well so that the alcohol evaporated and formed a gas in a confined container, you would get a sharp explosion if you dropped a lighted match into the can. *This is not an experiment you should try. It is too dangerous.*

Experiments like this, with alcohol, coal gas, turpentine vapor and other liquid vapors were being conducted in England and Europe throughout the time the steam engine was being perfected. But it was not until a hundred years after Watt patented his steam engine—in 1878—that a successful gas engine was invented. Its inventor was Nikolaus Otto, of Germany.

Except for the many refinements that have increased power and smoothed engine performance, the engine in your family automobile operates in basically the same way as did Otto's gas engine.

A gas engine is operated by a series of explosions. It is called an *internal-combustion* engine because the explosion, or the igniting of the fuel, takes place *within* the cylinder chamber. This is in contrast to the steam engine, where the combustion—that is, the boiling of the water to make the steam—takes place *outside* the cylinder. The steam engine, therefore, is an *external-combustion* engine.

These are the steps which take place in the cylinder of a gasoline engine. First, there is an intake stroke of the piston. This admits air into the cylinder and creates a vacuum at one point which draws in a fine spray of the fuel mixture, usually gasoline. The next stroke of the piston is a compression stroke, which packs the air and gasoline mixture into a small space. At this point an ignition spark, created

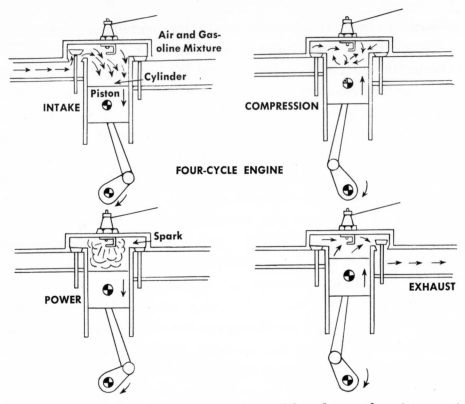

Air and Gas-
oline Mixture

Cylinder

Piston

INTAKE

COMPRESSION

FOUR-CYCLE ENGINE

Spark

POWER

EXHAUST

electrically, explodes the compressed gas. This drives the piston out in the third stroke, called the power, or expansion stroke. The fourth stroke is the exhaust stroke, which drives the consumed gas out of the cylinder and makes it ready for another four-stroke cycle.

THE DIESEL ENGINE

We all know the revolution in transportation that was made possible by the gas engine. But even more important to the progress of engineering was the development of another kind of internal-combustion engine—the Diesel. The inventor was Rudolf Diesel of Germany, whose first attempt at such an engine in 1893 resulted in an explosion that nearly killed him. Four years later, however, Diesel was able to build a successful model.

The Diesel engine differs from the gas engine in that the explosion is caused not by an ignition spark, but by the heat of highly compressed air. The Diesel engine uses crude oil, much cheaper than gasoline, as its fuel. On the downstroke of a Diesel piston, air is drawn into the cylinder under slight pressure. On the return stroke, the piston compresses this air to about one-fourteenth of its volume. This high compression raises the temperature of the air to about 1,000 degrees Fahrenheit. At this moment fuel oil is sprayed into the cylinder from a jet nozzle. Ignited by the hot air, the oil vapor explodes, driving the piston down in its power stroke. The fourth stroke, as in the gas engine, is an exhaust stroke, driving unburned gases out of the cylinder.

Although the Diesel engine is simpler and more efficient than the gas engine, it has been difficult to make these engines light enough to be practical for use in private automobiles. Diesels are used, however, in many heavy engineering jobs. Such engines operate power shovels, air compressors, irrigation pumps, electrical generators and similar heavy industrial machinery. Diesels also drive steamships, railroad locomotives, submarines, buses and heavy trucks.

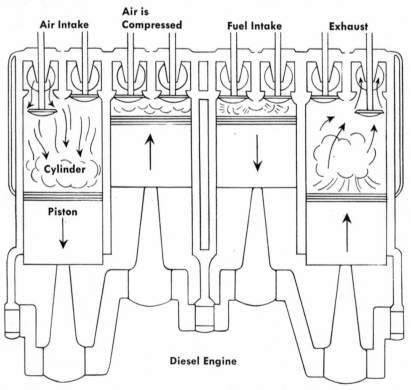

Diesel Engine

SOME PROBLEMS OF INTERNAL-COMBUSTION ENGINES

We must realize that the first gas and Diesel engines were very crude, and that the improvement of both types of internal-combustion engines was very slow. Both types of engines are still being improved today, and there is room for more improvement. From the standpoint of the engineer, neither engine is as efficient as the steam engine, since neither makes as full use of the potential energy of its fuel as does the steam engine. From the standpoint of convenient use, however, either type of internal-combustion engine is preferred, and that is why they have replaced the steam engine for most heavy-duty work.

The first internal-combustion engines were one-cylinder affairs, and they operated jerkily since only one out of every four strokes of the piston was a power stroke. Two-cylinder engines eliminated some of the jerkiness, and a fairly smooth operation was achieved when four-cylinder engines were designed, with the piston operations so timed that one of the four pistons was always delivering a power stroke. Later, the number of cylinders was increased, always in multiples of two. Automobile engines went from four to six, to eight, to 12, and finally to as many as 16 cylinders. As the efficiency of the various parts of the engine itself improved, however, it was unnecessary to have so many cylinders. The most powerful automobiles today have no more than eight cylinders. There are huge internal-combustion engines with as many as 24 cylinders, however. These are mainly in use on ships large enough to carry the weight of such engines.

Starting an internal-combustion engine presented problems which were not present in the steam engine. The first stroke of a steam engine began automatically as soon as the steam was introduced into the cylinder and was chilled and condensed to produce a vacuum. But the first two strokes of an internal-combustion engine required the turning over of the motor by means of a hand crank. It was not until the ignition fired the third, or power stroke, that enough momentum was given the flywheel to carry the piston through the exhaust, intake, and compression strokes again. Cranking an engine was dangerous, since the crank had to be dropped the moment the power stroke began. Many motorists suffered broken arms in those early days. Then engineers solved this problem, as they have so many others. An electric motor took over the job of starting the engine.

JET-PROPULSION ENGINE OF THE FUTURE

We usually think of progress as meaning that things get more and more complicated as they are improved. This is not always true. Often, the better ideas of the engineer result in simpler mechanisms. The jet engine is an example.

The easiest way to understand the principle of a jet engine is to blow up a balloon and let it escape from your fingers. The balloon will fly rapidly to the ceiling. Is it the air, escaping from the mouth of the balloon, that forces it up? No. If we remember our physics lessons we know that an expanding gas moves against a container in all directions. In the free balloon, the air, which acts like an expanding gas in this instance, is pressing against all sides of the balloon. It can only escape at the mouth. The pressure on the top and bottom and on the sides is equal, and thus is neutralized. At the mouth, where the air is escaping, there is no pressure on the inside surface of the balloon. Therefore, the pressure pushing on the end opposite the end where the air escapes will drive the balloon in the direction of that pressure.

A jet engine employs this principle. It is a streamlined shell of metal, inside which gases are formed by burning compressed air and liquid fuel. The gas is allowed to escape at one end of the engine, and the pressure, which thus pushes against the other end, drives the engine forward.

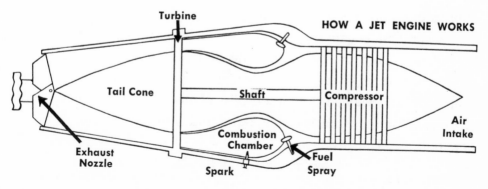

Turbine

HOW A JET ENGINE WORKS

Tail Cone   Shaft   Compressor

Air Intake

Combustion Chamber

Exhaust Nozzle

Fuel Spray

Spark

This is the basic idea; in actual practice the jet engine is a little more complicated. There is a turbine which compresses the air as it is admitted in the front of the engine. This turbine is connected by a shaft to a drive turbine which is operated by the gases formed when the air and the fuel are burned. After leaving the drive turbine, the gases escape from the rear of the engine. The diagram on the previous page of the stages of a jet engine will help make this clear to you.

Thus we find the engine of the future a very simple device. The basic operation is simply an application of a simple law of physics.

Jet engines are simple devices but they could not be made, however, until engineers had developed metals which would withstand high temperatures. The air taken in at the front of the engine may be as cold as 50 degrees below zero Fahrenheit at high altitudes. But when the air is compressed, and burned with the fuel, the gases are more than 1,500 degrees Fahrenheit.

Jet engines are used in military and commercial planes. There have been some experimental uses of jet engines for land vehicles, and they may be used for transcontinental trains in the future. Jet engines use a great deal of fuel, and their operation is too expensive for ordinary use.

A rocket engine is not the same as a jet engine. A jet engine mixes air with its fuel, and must constantly take on new supplies of air for the mixture. A rocket engine not only carries its fuel but also the oxygen to burn the fuel, and therefore does not require air. That is why we will use rocket engines, rather than jet engines, when we fly to other planets, crossing vast areas of space where the air is so thin as to be practically non-existent.

Since you began reading this book, you have seen man come a long way from the time when he first picked up a broken piece of quartz and, with the sharp edge, cut a point for a crude wooden tool. At first, it seemed that practically all men were trying to improve their tools and their ways of making and building things. Then we saw that, even in prehistoric times, there seemed to have been men who were better at toolmaking and hut-building than other men.

These men specialized in these tasks, trading the things they made and built for the food that other men hunted. These specialists in making things were the first engineers.

We have seen how men first learned to use the simple machines, then how he harnessed wind and water power, and finally how he made engines and motors, using the strange forces of electricity and expanding gases. We have seen how men improved their methods of making crude iron in a charcoal oven, by inventing furnaces which would turn out tons of fine steel for buildings and bridges.

Because we wanted to keep strictly to the record of important *engineering* milestones, we have not recorded many of the important scientific discoveries and inventions that you will find in your science books. We have tried to keep to the comparatively narrow path of engineering achievements alone. The time has now come to survey the miracles of modern engineering.

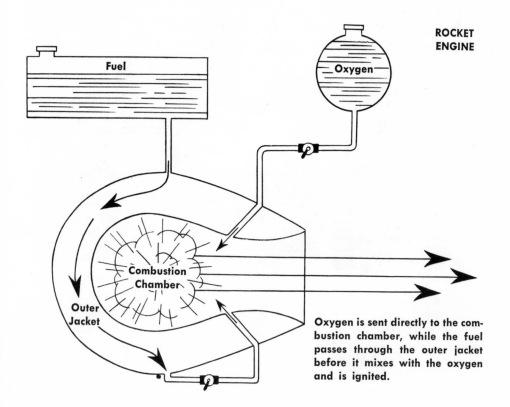

ROCKET ENGINE

Fuel

Oxygen

Combustion Chamber

Outer Jacket

Oxygen is sent directly to the combustion chamber, while the fuel passes through the outer jacket before it mixes with the oxygen and is ignited.

CHAPTER SIX

CIVIL ENGINEERING

IT is impossible to break up the big and busy field of engineering into completely separate divisions. No one man or woman would ever have the time, let alone the practical knowledge, to perform all the tasks which are done in the name of engineering. There are many specialists in engineering operations, and often they combine knowledge of two or three different fields to spend a lifetime career as *specialized specialists*. How, for instance, would you classify the engineer who specializes in planning, building and keeping in operation and repair the floating diesel-operated pumps used in mining along the shallow waters of our seacoasts? He might very properly be placed in civil engineering, in marine engineering, in stationary engineering, or he might be properly described as a mining engineer.

Having said that it is impossible to classify engineering tasks, we must nevertheless try to do this very thing, in order to fully survey the various fields into which a career in engineering may lead you. It is in much the same way that scientists classify every plant and animal in the world, even though, in many cases, they cannot decide whether certain specimens actually belong to the animal or to the plant world. Similarly, we must set up our definitions for the various fields of engineering, even though our definitions must often be arbitrary.

The biggest field in engineering is civil engineering, for civil engineers plan and construct every kind of big engineering project. Because the field of civil engineering is so big, it contains many subdivisions, and many specialists. Men who work on civil engineering projects one month can often be found in another branch of engineering, performing their special tasks, the following month.

The civil engineer is on the spot where a project is to be built long before construction starts. In fact, he is there even before sketches or blueprints are made. Surveying instruments are used to establish the exact boundaries of the project—the total area of land and/or water in which the project will be contained. And he also establishes the lines along which the physical structure will be built, since this structure usually takes up somewhat less space than the whole land area.

Long before building begins, the civil engineer has made his calculations in order to establish how strong a bridge must be, for example, to safely hold all the traffic it will carry during its busiest hours. It is he who decides what kind of a bridge it will be. His decision is based on the distance that must be spanned; the topography or nature of the land around the site; the weather conditions that usually prevail; the traffic or lack of traffic that will pass over and under the bridge, and a dozen other factors. For this problem, as for many others faced by engineers, there is no one best solution. There is no one best kind of bridge for all situations. But there is usually one best kind of bridge for the *particular* situation — and for the particular site on which this bridge is to be built.

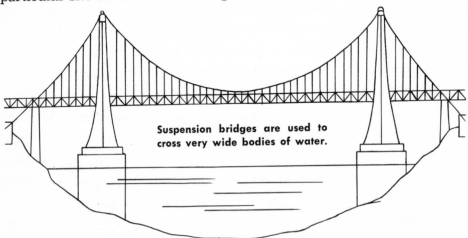

Suspension bridges are used to cross very wide bodies of water.

KINDS OF BRIDGES

The suspension bridge is the simplest kind of bridge to build, since it requires no piers to support it. The roadway of a suspension bridge is hung from and supported by cables. In order to get the main cables higher than the bridge, the cables are run over the top of high frames or towers at either end of the bridge, and the cables then are brought down to the ground and anchored in a huge mass of concrete. These main cables run from the tops of the towers down to the center of the bridge, then up to the top of the opposite tower. Smaller cables run down from the main cables to the roadway of the bridge, and take up part of the load.

The first step in building a suspension bridge is to build the steel-framed towers from which to run the cables. Farther back on the shore are the anchorages for the ends of the cables. These are huge blocks of concrete, sometimes as large as a big house. Inside these anchorages, laid there before the concrete is poured, are huge steel beams. These bars, projecting up through the concrete, end in rings through which the cable ends can be fastened.

If you ever get a closeup look at the cables of a suspension bridge, you will notice that the cables are from one to three feet thick, depending on the size of the bridge. These cables are made up of thousands of separate steel wires, each no thicker than the wire of an ordinary coat hanger!

A suspension bridge is started by getting just one of these wires across the river, canyon or valley that is to be bridged. That is, getting it from one anchorage, across the towers, and back to the anchorage on the other side. Wire after wire is "woven" across by a pulley wheel called a "traveling wheel."

It takes six or seven months, with crews working every day, to

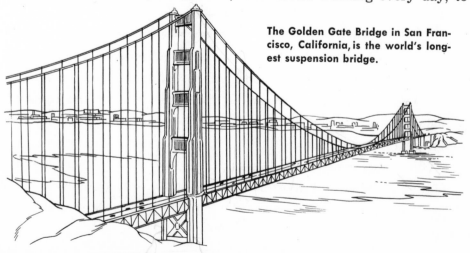

The Golden Gate Bridge in San Francisco, California, is the world's longest suspension bridge.

get enough wires back and forth across a river to build the cables of the average big suspension bridge. The wires have to be strung exactly right—so that they lie side by side, forming exactly the same arc from tower to tower. Otherwise, each wire would not support its share of the load as intended. When enough of the wires have been strung to make the cable, they are all wrapped together to form a single giant strand.

The longest suspension bridge in the world, the Golden Gate Bridge over San Francisco Bay (4,200 feet), is held up by main cables with a circumference of 3 feet. But each cable is formed of more than 27,500 strands.

The suspension bridge is the best means of bridging a river that is not only wide but also very deep, or one which has such a swift current that it would be difficult to sink piers into the river bed.

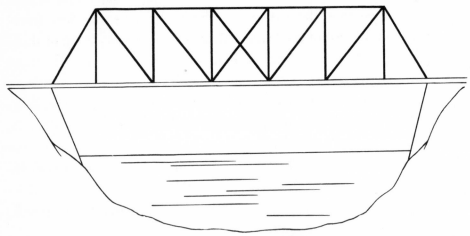

A truss bridge is the easiest way to span short distances.

The truss bridge is the simplest means of bridging short distances. In this type of bridge, the roadbed is supported on each side by a truss framework. This framework can be above the level of the roadbed or below it. It works just as well, doing its job of supporting the weight, in either position.

You can demonstrate the truss principle to yourself very simply by nailing together four short strips of wood to form an open square. Put just one nail at each corner to join the pieces. Now, hold the framework on end and press down. It is a simple matter to press the framework into a parallelogram instead of a square.

Now, push the framework back into a square and nail a fifth strip of wood across the square, diagonally. You will find it impossible to push the framework out of shape. You cannot do so because you

When a truss bridge spans a long distance, piers help support the weight. Pier bridges are sunk all the way down to bedrock.

have turned your square into two triangles. Triangles are stable— that is, they cannot be pushed out of shape unless they are broken Squares and rectangles are not stable—their corners form fulcrum points which yield to stress and strain.

A truss then, is a triangle, or a number of triangles made of wood or steel beams. Steel trusses are used on most modern bridges.

Often, truss beams on each side of the roadbed are strong enough

Example of Pier Bridge in Paris, France

to support a short bridge and the traffic that is to pass over it. When truss beams alone are not strong enough to do the job, then the problem is often solved by putting a few piers underneath the bridge to help support the weight.

Pier bridges require the sinking of piers into the river bed or down into the bottom of the chasm that is to be bridged. Sinking piers is difficult work, particularly in deep water. Below the water is a layer of soft mud, and below that is shifting sand. Below the sand is shale, a layer of loose, flat rock. It is necessary to go below the shale to get to bedrock, which is the only layer which will support the piers of a bridge that is to carry tons of weight in the form of moving trains, trucks and passenger automobiles.

Cofferdams are one means by which engineers sink foundations for piers. A cofferdam is like a big tube or open box of steel (it may be round or square in shape). The steel is driven deep into the mud of the river, until bedrock is struck. At this point, of course, the inside of the cofferdam is still filled with mud at the bottom, and above the mud is water to the level of the river. Scoops fastened to long cables dig out the mud, sand and shale from inside the cofferdam.

Now the bottom of the cofferdam must be sealed so that the water can be pumped out. This is accomplished by running a long pipe, called a *tremie pipe,* down one side of the cofferdam, almost to the bottom. A big round wooden plug is shaped to fit exactly inside the tremie pipe. When this plug is dropped into the top of the pipe, it floats at the top of the water inside the pipe, at the same level with the water inside the cofferdam. Next, concrete is poured into the pipe, on top of the wooden plug. The weight of the concrete pushes the plug down to the bottom, but the plug keeps the water from thinning the concrete on its way to the bottom of the tremie pipe. At the bottom of the tremie pipe, the plug is pushed out and bobs up to the surface of the cofferdam water. The concrete pours out of the tremie pipe and onto the bedrock at the bottom of the cofferdam.

This process is repeated until enough concrete has been poured around the bottom of the cofferdam to make a watertight seal. Now

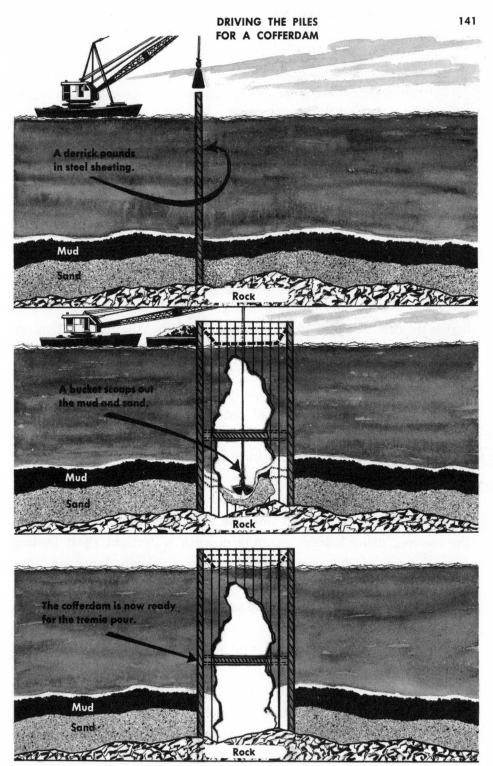

A cofferdam is the oldest device used to build a foundation under water. It is a watertight box which forms a frame into which cement will be poured.

all the water can be pumped from inside the cofferdam. Workmen go down to the concrete floor which is dry now, although it lies far below the surface of the river. They can begin to build the pier, making it rise above the surface of the river to the bridge it is to support.

Caissons must be used at depths and in currents where the pressure of the water is so great that it would break the steel walls of a cofferdam. You can get a rough idea of how a caisson works by pushing a glass straight down into a pan of water. You can see that the level of water inside the glass is lower than it is in the pan because the air pressure inside the glass is forcing the water level lower, creating a compressed air chamber inside the glass.

The caissons used in engineering are enormous steel boxes about the size of a 10-story building. A partition with openings extends across the caisson about 10 feet from the bottom. When these openings are closed, the partition is watertight.

When the caisson is lowered into the river, water runs up from the bottom and through the openings of the partition, coming up inside the caisson to the level of the surface of the river. When the openings are closed, however, and air is pumped into the caisson below the partition, water is forced out of the caisson below the partition. The bottom of the caisson, resting on the mud and sand of the river bottom, is full of pressurized air.

Workmen now descend into the air chamber at the bottom of the caisson, using ladders running down a watertight shaft leading from the top of the caisson. Before they go down, however, they enter an air lock at the top of this shaft, and the air pressure is gradually increased until it is the same as the pressure at the bottom of the caisson. At the bottom, the men use machinery to dig out the bottom of the river. The material they dig up is hauled to the top of the caisson through another watertight shaft.

Water is constantly trying to get in under the bottom edges of the caisson, and as the caisson sinks deeper, the air pressure must be increased in order to keep the water out. As the air pressure in the work chamber increases, it puts a great strain on the bodies of

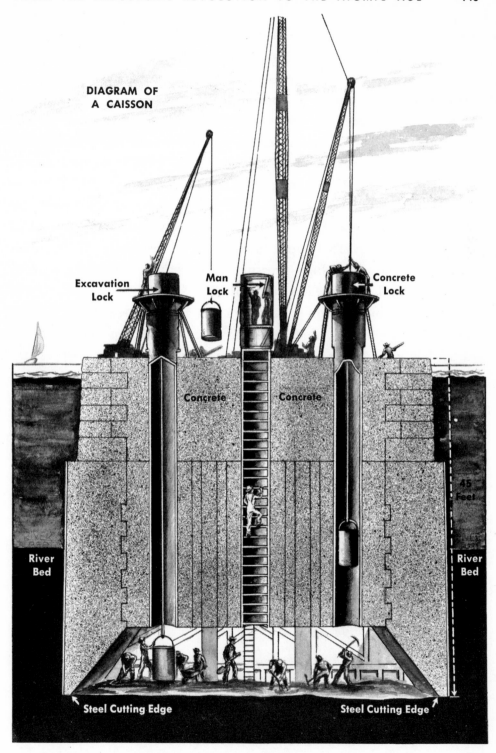

DIAGRAM OF
A CAISSON

Excavation
Lock

Man
Lock

Concrete
Lock

Concrete

Concrete

45
Feet

River
Bed

River
Bed

Steel Cutting Edge

Steel Cutting Edge

the workers. These men, called sandhogs, must keep in the best of physical condition. But even so, they can work for only short periods as the air pressure is increased, and their periods of resting and conditioning themselves in the air lock grow longer as the caisson sinks deeper. Sometimes, when the caisson goes down as far as 100 feet below the bed of the river, the sandhogs work less than half an hour, then rest six hours and work another half hour. At such depths the air pressure is 45 pounds per square inch.

Upon leaving the river bottom, the workers go up to the air lock, and there the air pressure is gradually lowered to normal atmospheric conditions. This must be done very gradually. If the men come out from under high pressure too fast, they develop a painful and often fatal disease called the "bends."

Working in a caisson is dangerous for another reason. All around the bottom of the big steel tube the river is swirling and churning away, trying to get inside and being kept out only by the air pressure inside the air chamber. Sometimes a soft spot develops at the edge of the caisson and the air escapes from the chamber, shooting men

This modern arch bridge has two roadways.

and equipment to the surface in a giant air bubble. Sometimes when this happens, men have been buried in the mud.

Modern arch bridges of steel or reinforced concrete can span much longer distances than the stonework arches of the ancient Romans.

Since an arch has no strength until the top, or keystone portion, is in position, any kind of arch bridge has to be supported until it is completed. This is done by building the steel or concrete arch over a lumber frame called a "falsework," or by supporting the halves of the arch with cables anchored on the shore until the top of the arch is completed.

The arch is always built first, and the roadway of the bridge is added later. Like the position of the trusswork in a truss bridge, it makes no difference how the strength of the arch is used. The roadway can go on top of the arch, or it may be hung below the arch. Or, the roadway can be partly supported by the arch and partly hung from it. These three ways of utilizing the arch in bridge building appear in the illustration on the opposite page.

Cantilever bridges balance the weight of truss sections, which are equal in size and shape, over a pier set in the river. That half, or arm, of the cantilever which is between the pier and the bank is called the *anchor arm*. The part on the river side of the pier is call the *cantilever arm*.

Combination bridges. The big bridge-building projects are often combinations of the various types of bridges we have discussed. The three-mile-long Triborough Bridge in New York City is a combination of five truss bridges, a suspension span and one span which lifts into the air to allow boats to pass under. The Transbay Bridge in San Francisco has two suspension spans, one cantilever span and five truss spans. This bridge is more than eight miles long. Long bridges like this become, in practice, a series of bridges, and the type of construction for each part is selected according to the conditions that exist for the area to be bridged.

Movable bridges are necessary where they span rivers which

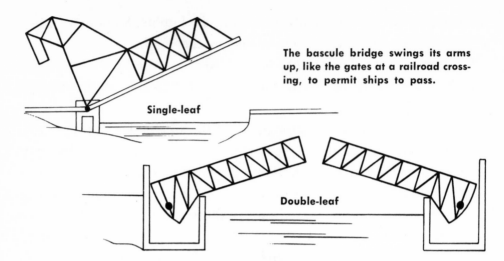

The bascule bridge swings its arms up, like the gates at a railroad crossing, to permit ships to pass.

Single-leaf

Double-leaf

are used by boats and ships whose masts and smokestacks could not pass under a fixed bridge.

The most common kind of movable bridge is the *single-leaf bascule bridge*. This kind of bridge is a modern version of the castle drawbridge of the Middle Ages. As you can see from the above drawing, a huge weight, usually of concrete, acts as a counterweight on the shore side of the bridge. This weight, plus the leverage of huge

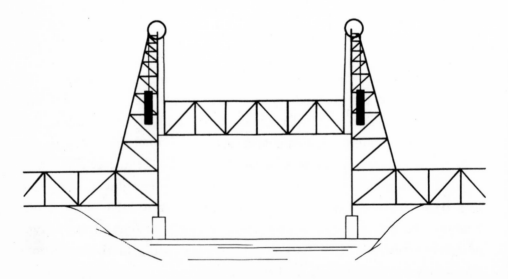

The vertical lift bridge raises up like an elevator to permit ships to pass underneath.

gears, makes it possible for a small amount of power, usually furnished by an electric motor, to raise the bridge. *Double-leaf bascule bridges* have two arms which meet over the center of the river when the bridge is down. Each arm raises up from the center when ships are passing through.

The swing, or turntable, bridge pivots on a pier in the center of a river to permit ships to pass.

For narrow streams which carry shipping, the *vertical lift bridge* is used. This is a truss bridge which raises and lowers by means of elevator shafts at either end.

The *swing bridge,* or *turntable bridge,* is pivoted on a pier in the center of the river. The bridge can be turned on its pier until it is parallel with the banks of the river, allowing water traffic to pass on either side of the pier. The pier takes up quite a bit of room in the center of the river, usually the deepest part. For this reason, swing bridges are used only where boats and smaller ships will need to pass through.

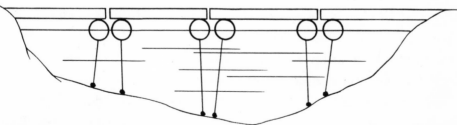

The pontoon, or floating bridge, has watertight tanks fastened underneath it in order to keep afloat.

Pontoon bridges, or *floating bridges,* have been used since ancient times. Pontoon bridges are usually temporary structures built by armies in order to transport troops after the enemy has bombed out the regular bridges. Watertight steel or aluminum tanks are fastened underneath the roadway of a pontoon bridge to keep it afloat. There are some permanent floating bridges, however. The largest of these crosses Lake Washington near Seattle, and carries four lanes of auto traffic. This bridge, a mile and a third long, is supported by hollow concrete pontoons. For concrete will float if it encloses a large enough volume of air—even small ships have been made of concrete.

Other famous bridges, in addition to the ones we have mentioned, are located all over the world. The largest steel arch bridge in the world is the Bayonne Bridge, connecting Staten Island, in New York Harbor, with New Jersey. Its span is 1,652 feet. It is an example of an arch bridge in which the roadway runs through the arch. A famous example of an arch underneath the roadway is the Rainbow Bridge between the United States and Canada, just below Niagara Falls. The steel arch spans 950 feet, and the roadway is 180 feet above the river.

Probably the highest bridge in the world is the Royal Gorge suspension bridge over the canyon of the Arkansas River in Colorado. This bridge hangs from mountain sides 1,053 feet above the river it spans. Cables anchored to the walls of the canyon keep this bridge from being lifted and bounced around by the high winds common in this mountain area.

Large bridges which use at once the arch, pier and truss in their construction include the 520-foot Eads Bridge over the Mississippi River at St. Louis, Missouri; the 977-foot Hell Gate Bridge in New York City; and the concrete-arched George Westinghouse Bridge which crosses a valley 1,510 feet wide near Pittsburgh, Pennsylvania.

The longest cantilever span ever built—1,800 feet across the St. Lawrence River in Canada—is the Quebec Bridge. This bridge collapsed twice during building because of engineering errors. Twice the original plans had to be redrawn, which caused the project to be delayed for 10 years. It has withstood the test of time, weather and traffic loads quite successfully, however, since it was completed and opened in 1917.

You will find the making of model bridges an interesting project. You will need only some strips of balsa wood such as are used in making model airplanes, some airplane glue and some small brad nails. By studying the pictures of the different kinds of bridges shown in this chapter, you can copy their essential construction. Balsa wood is easily cut with an ordinary pocketknife, and after it has been soaked in water, it can be bent into arches. The wood is so soft that the small brad nails can be pushed in with the handle of a pocketknife.

If your model bridge requires piers, you can make handsome ones from short lengths of softwood dowels. The roadways of your bridges can be flat strips of balsa wood, or whatever wood you desire. By using short nails as pivot points at the proper places on either side of your roadway, you can make a bascule bridge that will raise and lower like a real one, using a metal bolt or something of that nature to serve as a counterweight. Or, you can make a swinging bridge that will turn on a pivot mounted on a central pier. With small, light struts, you can copy the construction of the beautifully shaped cantilever bridges.

An interesting and inexpensive project that can be a great deal of fun is building a model bridge, using toothpicks and glue.

If you want to specialize in miniature models (which is much more painstaking work but can be a lot more fun, too) you should try making your models with toothpicks and glue. Use the round, smooth toothpicks—not the flat kind that taper sharply. You can even make the roadway of toothpicks joined together with airplane glue. It will take a long time, but you will be pleased with these beautiful little models, and they will attract a lot of comment from your friends. You have to be very patient, putting just a drop of glue on the ends of the toothpicks to be joined, and then you have to hold the ends together steadily until the glue is nearly dry.

Using fine wire for the cables, and a balsa wood framework for the suspension towers, you can even make a suspension bridge model.

If one of your bridge models turns out to be particularly fine, you may want to mount it in a natural setting. You can mold a miniature gorge or river valley, using a plasterlike material made by dropping equal quantities of salt and cornstarch into an old pan holding an equal volume of boiling water. Turn the fire out and stir the mixture until you have a mass like fine oatmeal. Before this cools, you can mold it into the shape you want, and place your bridge on the banks of the gorge or valley you have made. When the material is quite dry, you can paint it with brown, green and blue water colors to imitate natural surroundings. You can give your bridge a coat of red paint at the same time.

DAMS AND RESERVOIRS

Instead of bridging a stream or river, it is often the business of an engineer to block, or dam, its natural course and current.

The purpose of a dam is to increase the supply of water from a river at a given point. If the current of the river is blocked by a barrier of earth or stone, and a huge bowl, or reservoir, is dug behind the barrier, a supply of water can be collected behind the dam that is hundreds of times the volume of the water that would pass through the same point at any given time. A gate, or spillway, is put in the face of the dam. The spillway can be opened and regulated so that when the reservoir has been filled, the current of the river can continue to flow below the dam at its regular rate of flow, or at speeds greater or lesser than its regular rate of flow, as may be desired.

The water collected, or impounded, in the reservoir of a dam may be used for a number of purposes. Sometimes the water is stored in a very high reservoir so that it may fall through wheels or turbines which will drive the generators that produce electric power. Sometimes the same kind of reservoir holds water under high pressure, which is intended to be piped down to cities below the high reservoir.

Sometimes dams are built to collect water to irrigate nearby farmland during dry seasons. Quantities of water are released from the reservoir through irrigation ditches during dry seasons. During seasons of normal rainfall, or when crops are not being grown, the irrigation ditches are closed and the reservoir collects another supply of water.

Dams are also useful in controlling rivers which often flood their banks, causing damage to the farms, cities and towns along their course. When the river begins to rise to flood level, dam gates are closed and the river waters are held back until the flood danger is over.

Dams are often built to create artificial lakes, where fish and wild water birds can find a refuge, and which provide bathing and boating facilities for people of the community.

Dams are sometimes built for only one of these purposes, and other dams are built for several of these purposes. Multipurpose dams are particularly useful in the western part of the United States, where dams have turned desert areas into rich farmland, provided electric power for cities, and stored water for drinking and cooking purposes all at the same time.

Dams are also useful on rivers which can be navigated by ships and boats except for certain stretches where the water is not deep enough. Instead of dredging the shallow parts deeper, dams can be built which will build up the water over these parts so that ships can pass through. Of course, lock systems are made a part of such dam projects so that ships can negotiate the various water levels.

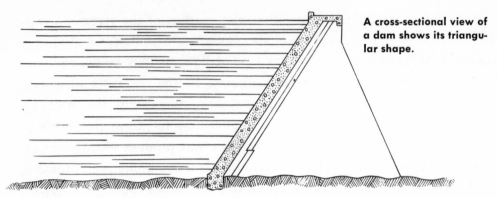

A cross-sectional view of a dam shows its triangular shape.

Shapes and Characteristics of Dams. We see very little of a dam after it is built. Only the crest, or top of the dam, and part of the structure are visible. Most of the dam is hidden by the water of the reservoir. If we could see the dam in cross section, however, we would see that engineers have made use of the strength in a triangle. That is, the base of the dam is much broader than the crest. Also, on large dams, we would see that the engineer had made use, in another direction, of the strength of an arch. The wide base, narrowing up to the crest, makes the triangle. The dam may also be arched across the stream, with the convex, or outside round, of the arch pointing upstream, against the current.

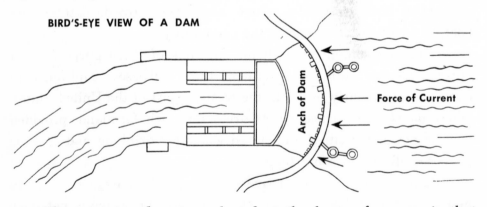

BIRD'S-EYE VIEW OF A DAM

Arch of Dam

Force of Current

The reason a dam is so broad at the base, of course, is that the pressure from the water stored in the reservoir is so much greater at the bottom than it is at the top. You can prove this yourself with a simple experiment that requires only a large tin container of some sort—a paint, varnish or oil can of about one gallon capacity. With a nail and hammer, punch three holes in the can, one hole near the top, one at about the middle of the can, and the third near the bottom. Cut one-inch squares out of some waterproof material—pieces of an old inner tube will do nicely. Now pour water into the can, and as the water passes over the lowest hole, put one of the squares of rubber over the hole on the inside of the can. The pressure of the water will hold the square of rubber tightly against the inside of the can. Do the same thing with the other squares just as the water reaches the holes to be plugged.

When the can is full of water, reach down inside and slide the top square of rubber away from the hole for a moment. Notice how far the tiny stream of water spurts through this hole. Replace the top square quickly, and uncover the middle hole. Cover this again, and uncover the bottom hole. You'll be surprised at how much farther the water spurts out of the bottom hole, compared to the stream thrown from the middle hole, which in turn is farther than the stream thrown from the top hole.

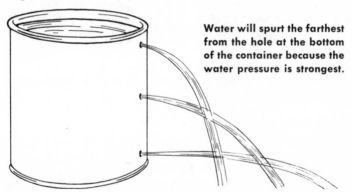

Water will spurt the farthest from the hole at the bottom of the container because the water pressure is strongest.

The weight of a column of water one inch square and one foot deep is figured as .43 of a pound. The pressure exerted by this column of water at a depth of one foot, or at the bottom of its own volume, is said to be .43 pounds per square inch. But this same column of water weighs twice as much, and exerts twice as much pressure, at a depth of two feet. At a three-foot depth, the pressure is three times as great, or 1.29 pounds per square inch; at 10 feet it would be 4.3 pounds per square inch.

You can see then, that the pressure against the bottom of a 600-foot dam, holding back many thousands of gallons of water representing millions of columns of water, would be very great indeed.

As a general working rule, the base of a dam should be as broad as is necessary to make the slope of the dam from base to crest a 45-degree angle. With this angle constant, the base of the dam will increase in proportion as the height increases.

Hoover Dam is the largest dam in the United States. Located on the Arizona-Nevada border, it supplies water to Los Angeles, 250 miles away.

The construction of a large dam is quite a big engineering project, requiring many men and machines and tons of materials. But the methods and materials used are quite ordinary. Many large dams are *earth fill*. They are made only of earth and rock, dumped into the water and then piled high above the banks by power machinery. There is a certain art, however, in the application of the dirt and rock. Coarse, heavy material is placed on the outsides of the dam, while the finer material is dumped in the center. Heavy power rollers press each load of earth tightly down. This kind of a dam, called a *roll fill* dam, is subject to a certain amount of leakage, and is not used for dams required to hold back large amounts of water. Sometimes earth fill dams have a thin inner core of concrete, which makes them waterproof.

Hydraulic fill dams are built by mixing earth and rock with water, and flushing the mixture into the site of the dam through pipes under high pressure. This method packs the material in tightly, and when the water drains and dries out, the dam is tight and waterproof. The outsides of the dam are finished with a facing of concrete, stone, timber and sometimes steel plates.

The largest dams, of course, are entirely of masonry construction —that is, of stones held together by mortar, or of concrete poured into wooden forms which are later removed.

Perhaps you have access to some property through which a small stream runs. If you can get permission, you might find it fun to build a small dam which will back up the stream and form a pool for wading, sailing toy boats, or which might even be stocked with fish.

The hardest part of building such a dam will be the construction of a form of lumber like that shown on the next page. The way the lumber is nailed together and then braced with ties of twisted wire is clearly shown in the drawing. You can then fill this form with concrete. A 1:3:4 mix is advised for waterproof quality—that is, one part of Portland cement, three parts of sand and four parts of gravel.

Mixing enough concrete for even a small dam is a lot of work and quite expensive. You may choose, instead, to build your dam of rocks and earth, putting the biggest rocks on the outside of your dam and filling in the center with a mixture of small stones and earth.

CANALS AND LOCKS

The building of canals is another way in which engineers make water work for man. People who do not live near an inland waterway sometimes think of canals as belonging to the romance of the past when canal boats were pulled by horses on the banks.

But canals are more important to us today than they were before the coming of the railroad and all the modern means of transportation. Today, great ship canals make it possible for thousands of miles to be

A dam built at home could provide a wading pool, or a private "fishin' hole."

saved in the sailing distances of freight steamers, and inland canals and waterways are still the cheapest and most convenient way of shipping heavy goods.

Put in the simplest terms, a canal is just a big ditch containing enough water to float a ship or boat. The bed of the canal must be level, or nearly level, so that no current will develop.

Canals often connect two bodies of water, such as a lake and a river, or two rivers, to one another, or they may even link an ocean with a lake to a sea and other ocean. Often, however, short canals are merely short cuts along the course of a navigable river. Many rivers are suitable for boats and ships except in certain places where they bend in huge arcs for many miles, or rush over a waterfall where boats cannot pass. In such places, a short canal may be built to bypass the trouble. Canals often are used to pass boats around the site of a dam which has been built across a navigable river.

Only very short canals are of the simple ditch type. Canals of any length require *locks* to raise and lower the water so that canals can be operated over sections where the ground level rises and falls.

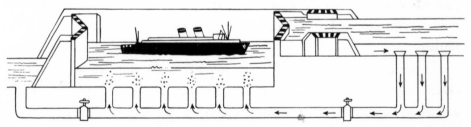

The ship enters the lock and a gate seals off the water between the lock and the level of the water. Water is then pumped into the lock until the boat reaches the next level of water. The ship then passes into the next lock. The same process occurs until the ship passes into open water.

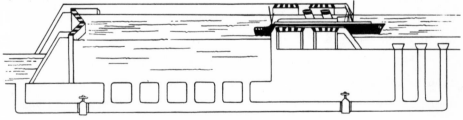

How a Canal Lock Works. When a change in the ground level occurs in the course of a canal, the bed of the canal is dug on two different levels, one higher than the other. At the point where the beds should meet, but cannot, because they are not on the same level, a lock is built. A lock is a watertight box, of steel, stone or concrete. Its walls begin at the bed of the lower level of the canal and rise to a point above the level of the water in the higher level of the canal.

When a ship or boat wishes to pass from the lower level to the higher level of the canal, it enters the lock and a gate seals off the water between the lock and the lower level. Now water is pumped into the lock until the boat is raised to the water line on the higher level of the canal. A gate is opened on this side of the lock, and the boat passes into the higher level of the canal.

When a ship or boat needs to pass from the higher level to the lower level, water is pumped into the lock chamber to receive the vessel, and then is let out until the boat sinks to the water line of the lower level of the canal.

This, of course, is the simplest kind of canal lock. Canals which pass over sharply rising ground require a series of locks, with enormously complicated mechanisms. The principle of these complicated multiple locks, however, is the same as that we have described.

Locks are the canal engineer's answer to changes in ground level. Over valleys or gullies, where the change is from higher to lower and then back to higher ground again, an aqueduct is usually built. The bed of the canal is carried across a series of arches from one side of the valley to another. In the same way, locks are not usually constructed to carry a canal over a ridge or hill. Instead, the canal would be dug through the hill, or if this were too big a project, it might circle around it.

Great Ship Canals. The St. Lawrence Seaway demonstrates how canals, linked to natural waterways, can allow ocean-going ships to penetrate to the heart of a continent. This seaway allows ocean vessels to enter the mouth of the St. Lawrence River in Quebec, Canada, and

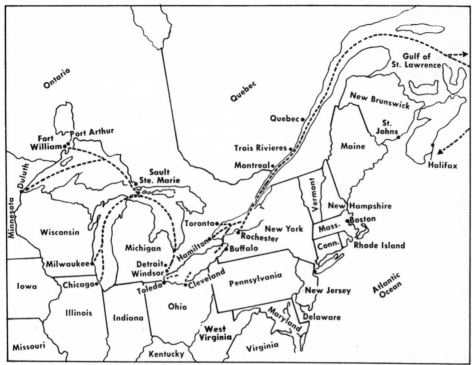

The St. Lawrence Seaway permits ocean-going vessels to reach inland ports.

travel up the river to the Great Lakes to reach ports as far south and west as Whiting and Gary, Indiana, in the heart of the nation's steel-production area.

The largest ocean freighters can now bring their cargoes directly to Middle Western ports. It is no longer necessary to unload the cargoes in New York, Boston, or other Eastern seaboard cities, and then transfer the cargo to railroad cars for the trip inland.

While most of the route of the St. Lawrence Seaway is over natural water routes, the seaway would not be passable without the dozens of canals which link these waterways, carrying the ships past shallow stretches, rapids and around waterfalls and dams.

The importance of ship canals was demonstrated to the world in 1956 when the Suez Canal was blocked to shipping, following a dispute among Egypt, Israel, France, England and the United States over the operation of the canal.

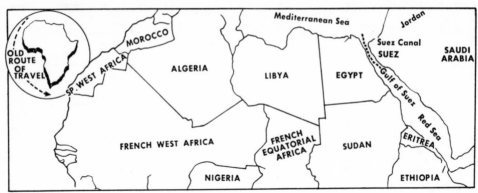

Before the Suez Canal was built, ships had to make a long voyage around the tip of Africa.

Take a look at the map of Asia and you will quickly agree that Nature did not have sailors in mind when the Mediterranean Sea and the Red Sea were shaped. The Mediterranean has an outlet to the Atlantic Ocean, and the Red Sea is an arm of the Pacific. The Mediterranean and the Red Sea almost meet—there is only a little more than 100 miles of land between them. But because of this arm of land—the Isthmus of Suez—ships had to sail 6,000 miles around the continent of Africa to take goods from ports east and south of the Mediterranean in order to reach England and the continent of Europe.

Kings and conquerors saw the advantage of a canal cutting across this arm of land and mariners thought longingly of such a canal for hundreds of years. But the canal was not started until 1859, and it took ten years to complete.

The Suez Canal has no locks, since there is no great difference between the water levels of the Mediterranean and the Red Sea, and the land through which the canal passes is flat Egyptian desert. Dredges are constantly operated in the canal to keep it free of sand blowing in from the desert.

When the Suez Canal is blocked, as it was for a time during the dispute over its operation, serious shortages of oil, coal, foodstuffs and other supplies develop in England and Europe because of the extra time needed for ships to make the long voyage around the tip of Africa.

The Panama Canal is another ship canal that enormously shortens voyages for merchant ships. This canal cuts through the Isthmus of Panama, a narrow strip of land that not only connects the continents of North and South America, but also serves to divide the Atlantic and Pacific Oceans. By Panama Canal, the voyage to the Pacific is only a little over 50 miles. It would be 7,873 miles long if it were necessary to sail around South America!

While the Panama Canal is less than half as long as the Suez Canal, it was a much bigger job from an engineering standpoint. The Panama Canal has an elaborate system of locks, and ships are pulled through the locks by electric locomotives running over tracks along the banks.

The job of digging the Panama Canal involved removing about 240,000,000 cubic yards of earth, which engineers have estimated, would be enough to build a wall five feet thick and 10 feet high entirely around the world! The story of the hardships and difficulties encountered as the Panama Canal was built by Army engineers between 1904 and 1920 is a thrilling and adventurous one. You may want to do some additional reading on this.

Canals play an interesting part in the Atlantic Intracoastal Waterway, a sheltered route for small pleasure boats and some small

The Panama Canal links the Atlantic Ocean with the Pacific Ocean.

cargo vessels. This waterway is a chain of canals, rivers, lakes, bays and inlets extending from New York Harbor to the tip of Florida. Although the waterway is within sight of the rough waters of the Atlantic Ocean most of the time, the waterway itself is usually calm and smooth. Those parts of the waterway which do lie in the ocean itself are protected from rough waves by islands, sandbars and break-waters. There are about 100 bridges along the waterway. Most of them are movable to allow boats to pass. The others are built high enough to allow boats to pass underneath. One of the longest canals in the waterway is the one that travels through the Dismal Swamps of North Carolina and Virginia. Here locks are needed to lift and lower boats to various levels. Boats are guided through the waterway by 22 lighthouses and nearly 4,000 floating channel markers. The waterway would not have been feasible without canals.

IMPORTANT CANALS IN THE UNITED STATES

NAME	LOCATION
Cape Cod	Massachusetts
Champlain	New York
Chesapeake and Delaware	Maryland-Delaware
Chicago Sanitary and Ship Canal	Illinois
Beaumont-Port Arthur Ship Canal	Texas
Houston	Texas
Lake Washington Ship Canal	Washington
Louisville and Portland	Kentucky
New Orleans Industrial	Louisiana
New York State Barge Canal	New York
St. Lawrence Waterway	United States-Canada
Sault Sainte Marie	Michigan
The Dalles	Oregon

There are about 21,000 canals of various types and lengths in the world. More than half of these canals are in Europe. Canals linking the many rivers of Europe form an important part of the transportation system on that continent. But there is an increasing use of canals within the United States, too, in spite of the many other modern forms of transportation in which this country excels, since slow water transportation is the cheapest way to move bulky shipments which can be ordered well in advance of the need.

TRANSPORTATION BY RAIL

Nowhere has the role of the engineer been more important than in the building of railroads, subways, elevated train systems and other forms of transportation on rails. In addition to the engineering involved in railroad construction and operation in itself, these systems involved bridges, tunnels and traffic interchanges as well.

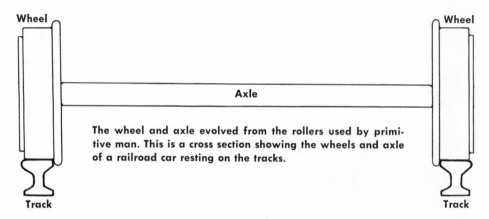

The wheel and axle evolved from the rollers used by primitive man. This is a cross section showing the wheels and axle of a railroad car resting on the tracks.

The principle of running vehicles with flanged wheels over rails was established long before there was any steam engine or other mechanical means of power to move the vehicle. Donkeys, hitched to small carts running on wooden or iron rails, pulled loads out of the mines and quarries of England and Europe during the Middle Ages. The first street cars in the United States were pulled by horses.

Rails were cheaper to lay than smooth pavement—they made it easier for animals to pull huge loads, and where there were passengers involved, they made the ride more comfortable. The cars required no steering—the flanged wheels made the cars follow the rails wherever they led. Anyone who has had an electric train set or who has the opportunity to see a train closely knows what a flanged wheel is.

The flanges, extending beyond the rim of the wheel on the inside of each track, keep the train on the track with a minimum of friction.

The railroad began in England, with the mine carts we told you about. In England, too, the first steam-powered locomotive was put on rails by Richard Trevithick in 1804. Trevithick's locomotive was little more than a curiosity which people paid admission to see run around a small circular track. The first practical locomotive was built in 1814 by George Stephenson, who is accepted by most historians as the "father of the locomotive." His locomotive ran on rails for nine miles from a coal mine to a seaside wharf where the coal the locomotive hauled could be loaded on ships.

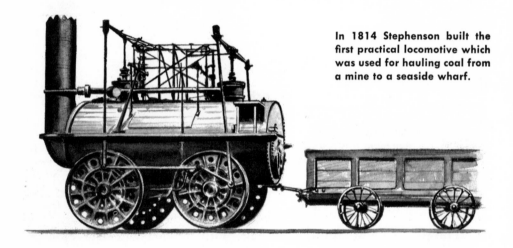

In 1814 Stephenson built the first practical locomotive which was used for hauling coal from a mine to a seaside wharf.

The first railroad in the United States, a 13-mile stretch of rails constructed by the Baltimore and Ohio Stage Company, used cars pulled by horses. It was opened for passenger and freight transportation in 1830, the same year that the South Carolina Railroad began experimental trips with a steam locomotive, "The Best Friend of Charleston." By 1833 the South Carolina Railroad had a real service in operation over the 136 miles between Charleston, South Carolina, and Hamburg, near Augusta, Georgia.

But the development of the locomotive itself is not as interesting to students of engineering as are the problems which had to be solved and the accompanying projects that needed to be built in extending the railroads over longer distances.

The railroad builders quickly learned to make their roadbeds as level as possible. A locomotive cannot pull a load up a grade which rises more than five feet in a hundred feet of track (a 5 percent grade). And even so, such a grade puts too much strain on the locomotive. Few railroads have grades of more than 2 percent (that is, the rails do not rise more than two feet in a hundred feet of track). Even today's railroads, with their powerful diesel engines, try to keep their grades within .5 per cent (rising only about six inches for every hundred feet of track).

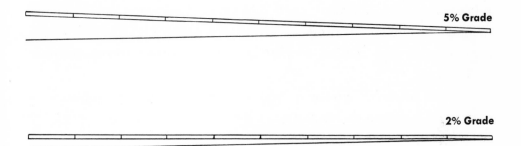

5% Grade

2% Grade

The need to keep the roadbeds level created many difficult engineering tasks. Long trestles had to be built across even very shallow valleys; mountains had to be tunneled through; rivers and canyons had to be bridged.

Cities and towns used to take pride in having a railroad pass through their community. But with truck and automobile traffic so heavy in modern times, railroad crossings have become traffic hazards and bottlenecks. Now, engineers raise or lower tracks where they enter cities. In New York, for instance, the tracks leading to Grand Central Station are buried in tunnels below the surface of the earth. In smaller cities, the railroad tracks are often elevated, and the streets and highways pass beneath them.

Railroads, once laying miles of new tracks in every direction, have reached their full growth in the United States today. No new railroad companies are being started, and few track extensions are being made by present roads. Railroads today compete for the nation's transportation business with trucks, buses, airplanes and ships.

But railroads are still a highly important part of the transportation picture. They undoubtedly will continue to be important, and to need the services of many kinds of engineers.

Civil engineers plan and supervise the building of a new railroad, bridges, tunnels and spur lines to serve new industries. Maintenance engineers keep the locomotives, cars and tracks in good repair. Electrical engineers maintain and improve the elaborate signaling and communications systems of the modern railroad. Engineers design and build the many special kinds of cars used in freight shipments— refrigerator cars for meat, fruit and other foods that spoil quickly without refrigeration; automobile cars; tank cars for oil and chemicals; cars for carrying molten metals; and many other special-purpose freight cars.

As an engineer, you may find yourself making contributions to the railroad system no matter what field you have chosen.

TUNNELS AND SUBWAYS

We have learned how ancient man dug shafts into the earth, then tunneled away from the shaft, in search of better flints below the surface. We know, too, that ancient man knew the difficulties and dangers in digging tunnels. The miners soon learned to "shore up" the walls of their tunnels with timbers, and to support the roofs with timbers or pillars. In the coal mines of England, the *room and pillar* method of mining was developed. Instead of digging out all of the coal in a mine, the English miners would leave huge columns of coal as supporting pillars, and take the coal from a series of "rooms" created by this method. This left a lot of good coal in the mine, but the safety afforded by the method was felt to be more than worth this loss.

Tunneling was confined to mines, to some secret passageways dug beneath the castles of the Middle Ages and to some city sewer systems which, like the sewers of Paris, ended in a series of tunnels.

But these kinds of tunnels were relatively simple, requiring only firm soil and the labor of men with shovels and buckets.

Tunneling did not become an engineering project until men needed to go under rivers and through mountains, and to go beneath the streets of cities to build subways for considerable distances.

Cutting a tunnel through solid rock is no particular problem, except for the labor involved. The rock sides support the roof of the tunnel, particularly if the roof is arched.

Digging a tunnel through soft earth and sand, or even mud, is a much more difficult project. You know this to be so if you have ever dug tunnels in the sand at the beach. No matter how carefully you try, there comes a time when the soft sand caves in, ruining your tunnel. But you may have solved the problem the way many young- sters have learned to do—if you have a number of tin cans with both ends cut away you can put these inside your tunnel to support the roof as you dig out the tunnel.

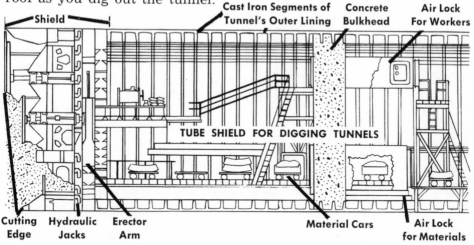

TUBE SHIELD FOR DIGGING TUNNELS

Engineers use the same principle in digging tunnels in soft mud. A huge steel tube, called a shield, is put in place after a shaft has been dug into the ground where the tunnel is to begin. The shield is a cylinder, except for the front, which is bent to form a sharp, bladelike edge. Powerful jacks, extending from the shield, dig into the ground outside the shield and push it through.

In going through soft material beneath rivers, the shield would be flooded with water, and the workmen in it drowned, unless the water was forced out of it with jets of compressed air.

A simple demonstration of how this is done can be made with a soda straw and a glass of water. Put the straw in the water and you will see that water gets into the straw up to the level of the water in the glass. But you can keep the water out of the straw by blowing on it. We have already studied this principle at work earlier in this chapter, when we learned how caissons were used to sink the foundations for bridge piers.

As the shield works its way through mud and silt, the walls of the permanent tunnel are built behind it. The tunnel walls may be of steel plates, of brick, building stone, or concrete. Tunnels are usually cylindrical in shape, because of the greater strength this gives the walls. The strength of an arch is presented against the pressure of the earth in every direction.

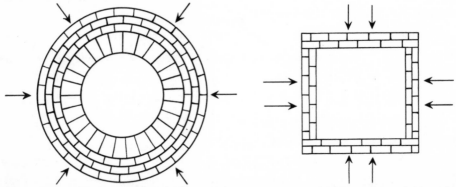

These cross sections of tunnels compare the strength of a rectangle and a cylinder. The latter has the strength of an arch pushing against the pressure of the earth in all directions.

The shield method of digging tunnels is used chiefly in digging beneath the beds of rivers. In digging other kinds of tunnels, however, the shield is not always necessary. Another tunneling method used is the *cut and cover* method. The tunnel is dug as if it were a deep ditch; the floor and walls of the tunnel then are built, and finally a roof is put on. Earth is then shoveled on top of the roof. Tunnels which are to carry railroad tracks beneath streets and highways are often built in this manner.

When a river bed is fairly hard and stable, it is often unnecessary to tunnel beneath it. Instead, sections of a steel tunnel can·be laid in the water, resting on top of the bed, and then joined together.

Shafting is another method of digging short tunnels. Shafts are dug straight down at short intervals, and sections of the tunnel are dug and completed between the shafts.

Some Famous Tunnels. The first serious attempt to tunnel beneath a river was begun in London in 1804. After the shaft had been dug 76 feet under the Thames River, Richard Trevithick, whom we know as the first man to put a steam locomotive on tracks, was hired to help with the work. Trevithick and his crew had no shield and no compressed air. They simply built up the rock-walled tunnel as they dug. When water from the unwalled end of the cut seeped into the tunnel, they used a steam engine to pump it dry enough so that they could continue their work. The shaft had been dug 1,000 feet under the Thames before the roof broke through and the river flooded the tunnel.

A second tunnel was begun under the Thames in 1824. Marc Brunel, a French engineer who fled to England during the French Revolution, built a crude shield of cast-iron which protected the men as they dug out the tunnel and built its brick lining. The shield was pushed ahead by crude screw jacks such as we use today to jack up automobiles for repairs. This shield was fairly successful as long as it worked through clay. But when it struck mud and silt the river poured in and destroyed the tunnel several times. A second shield was built and the tunnel was completed in 1843, nineteen years after the work began.

The tunnel was a curiosity for a time, but Londoners soon gave up walking through it, and crossed the river by bridge instead. No approaches were ever built for carriage or wagon traffic. Finally the tunnel was closed, and was not opened until 20 years later, when railroad tracks were laid through it and the tunnel became a part of the London Underground, or subway system.

The use of compressed air to keep water from entering the tunnel under construction was introduced by DeWitt Clinton Haskin, who began work on the first tunnel under the Hudson River in New York City. Haskin, who started work on the tunnel in 1874, did not use a shield. Instead, he installed an air lock at the mouth of the tunnel, and filled the tunnel itself with compressed air to keep the water out. This meant that the workmen had to work in compressed air. There were so many difficulties involved in using this method, however, that it was abandoned after several serious accidents. A group of English engineers then took over the project, but the backers ran out of money and the tunnel was flooded when work stopped in 1891. Later, American engineers took over the English equipment and finished the tunnel in 1904, thirty years after the project was first started. This was the North Tube of the Hudson River tunnel between New York and New Jersey. The South Tube was built afterward, with much less trouble, since the method of using a shield together with compressed air had been worked out.

Tunnels had been cut through solid rock during the Middle Ages, particularly in the mountain regions of Europe. But it was a long, hard task. One man would hold a chisel against the rock face while another struck the tool with a hammer. As soon as a hole had been made large enough to hold a charge of gunpowder, a portion of the rock face would be blasted away. Then the broken rock would be cleared away and another hole would be started for a new charge of gunpowder. This was an improvement over the methods of ancient miners, who tunneled into rock by building a fire against the rock face, then dashing cold water against the heated rock. But tunneling through rock remained a laborious and expensive undertaking until 1857, when work was begun on a tunnel through the Alps Mountains between France and Italy.

For centuries the Alps had made travel difficult between France, Italy and Switzerland. Only in good weather was it possible to go through passes between the tall, rugged mountains. In winter the passes were closed by snow. Yet Hannibal crossed the Alps in 218 B.C.

to attack the Roman Empire. And Charlemagne and Napoleon, among other conquerors, led troops over the mountains into Italy.

Napoleon began the work of building carriage roads through the mountains in 1803; but these roads were passable only during good weather. When railroads were built in Europe, they stopped on either side of the Alps. Passengers had to leave their trains and make their connections on the other side of the mountains by means of carriages, which could make the trip only when the passes were open.

As early as 1450, men had tried to tunnel through the Alps, but the job was soon given up as impossible. In 1838, a tunnel was again proposed by Joseph Medail, an Italian contractor who lived near the Swiss border. Medail had noticed that the narrowest part of the mountain wall separating the countries on either side of the Alps occurred in Mount Cenis. Medail had also noted that the land on one side of this mountain was on the same level as the land on the other side.

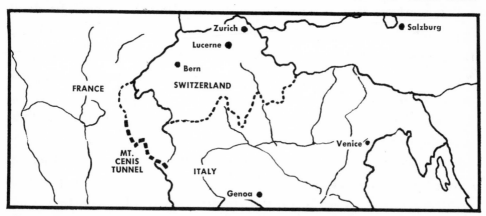

The Mt. Cenis Tunnel, dug through solid rock, was the world's longest tunnel when first built.

Practical engineers were intrigued with Medail's idea. But there were many who felt that the job was too huge. Up to that time, the longest tunnel that had ever been built was only two miles long. And Medail was proposing a tunnel that would be eight miles long, and cut through solid rock. There was no way in which shafts could be sunk at intervals to help guide the work—this tunnel would have to be dug for four miles from either end, and the two crews would have to meet in the middle!

While the argument was going on, engineers in England developed a new machine for drilling holes in rock. This machine operated using compressed air, which sent a pointed drill in and out of the rock face with rapidly repeated strokes, quickly making holes which could be filled with gunpowder. The air was compressed by a steam engine. The steam engine itself could not be used to operate the drill because quick, delicate, yet powerful blows were needed. But compressed air was found to furnish just the right power for the job.

The tunnel builders, or rather those who were thinking about building the Mount Cenis Tunnel, quickly saw that the steam-operated compressed-air drill was not the answer to their problem. It was pointed out that the steam engine necessary to compress the air would fill the tunnel with steam and make it impossible for men to work there.

Engineering students at the University of Turin in Italy were put to work on this problem. They decided that the pneumatic drills could be operated by hitching them to flexible hoses filled with air compressed *outside* the tunnel. The air could be compressed by a steam engine or by water power. It was decided to use water power, since it was plentiful in the mountains.

The drilling of the tunnel was begun by hand, at each end, while the compressed air equipment, the drilling machines and the gunpowder plants were set up around the tunnel project. Drilling by hand, the workers at either end of the tunnel were able to progress about 5 feet per week. When the air drills went into operation, each end of the tunnel advanced 36 feet per week.

Today, because of improvements in drilling equipment, engineers can drive tunnels through rock at the rate of nearly 300 feet per week!

The Mount Cenis Tunnel, measuring 7.97 miles in length, was the longest tunnel in the world when it was first built. Now it is surpassed by several others, including the 12.45-mile Simplon Pass Tunnel between Italy and Switzerland, and by the Pennsylvania Railroad Tunnel to New York, which runs under the Hudson River for 1¼ miles of its total length of 11.7 miles.

While it is not among the longest of rock tunnels, one of the most interesting from an engineering standpoint is the Moffat Tunnel, in Colorado. This tunnel cuts through James Peak, a part of the Continental Divide, at a height above sea level of 9,200 feet. The Moffat Tunnel is really two tunnels—one 16 feet wide and 24 feet high—through which trains run. This tunnel shortens the distance between Salt Lake City, Utah, and Denver, Colorado, by 175 miles. In addition to shortening the distance for railroads, the tunnel makes it possible for trains to avoid the snowstorms, snowslides and steep grades which formerly made transportation across the mountain divide costly and uncertain. The other tunnel, 8 by 8 feet, carries water from the Fraser River to the city of Denver. The length of the Moffat Tunnel is 6.11 miles.

Subways are really tunnels for underground city railway systems. They are built much like any other tunnel—either by the open cut, or ditch method, or by boring with a shield. The engineering problems are much the same whichever method is used. Cities which have subway systems include New York, Chicago, Boston, Philadelphia, London, Paris, Moscow, Tokyo, Berlin, Madrid, Barcelona, Buenos Aires and Sydney.

Subway systems are an excellent means of public transportation in a big city, because they take a great part of the traffic load off the city's streets and put it underground. In the subway tubes, schedules cannot be disrupted by snowstorms or other weather disturbances which cause delays in transportation above ground.

The first subway was built in London in 1863. Boston began the first subway in the United States in 1897. New York City's subway system was begun in 1904, and today that city has about 240 miles of subway, the longest system in the world.

A 22-mile tunnel between France and England, under the English Channel, has been planned since the early 1800's. Digging actually began on both sides of the channel in 1880. But the project was stopped for fear the tunnel would be used as a means of invading England from Europe. During World War II a watch was placed over the old tunnel mouths, and electronic listening devices were trained to catch the sound of boring from underneath the channel, in case the enemy should try to dig a tunnel secretly.

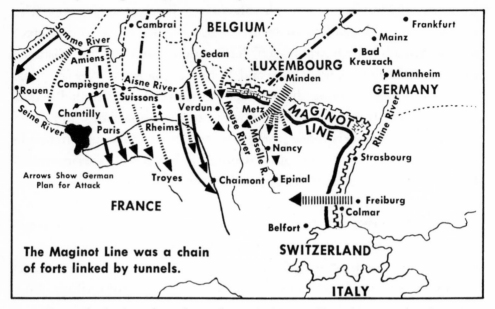

The Maginot Line was a chain of forts linked by tunnels.

Tunnels have played, and probably will continue to play, an important part in military engineering. Just before World War II, France depended on the Maginot Line for defense. This chain of forts was linked by tunnels and supplied from underground chambers where soldiers lived and in which ammunition was stored. But the Maginot Line fell before the swift attack of the German motorized army, which raced between the forts after the German air force bombed part of the chain into surrender.

At Fort Knox, Kentucky, a series of tunnels and underground chambers guard our defense secrets and military plans, as well as a large part of the U. S. Treasury's gold supply. And tunnels are expected to be the safest kind of shelter against atomic attack. Many of them are being built as part of city civil defense programs.

STREETS, ROADS AND HIGHWAYS

The Romans had established the characteristics of a good road long before the fall of their empire. Their roads had all the main features of our roads today — a crown at the center, sloping away on both sides so that water would drain off, and shoulders at the sides of the road proper, leading down to drainage ditches. The Romans knew the importance of a good bed for the surface of a road. It remained for modern engineers to improve methods for building roads over long distances, to speed up their construction and to develop better road-building materials.

But it was a long time before road building became the important engineering activity it is today. Stones, bricks and blocks of wood served as paving materials during centuries of European history. Long-distance roads were made of gravel or pounded earth. Horses pulled wagons and carriages over them quite well in dry weather, but when the roads became impassable in winter, people and goods stopped moving over land.

In North America the development of road building was just as slow, and for a long time, it was well behind the advances made in Europe. The first colonies huddled close together on the Eastern coast, had less need of roads as they could communicate by sea.

When the explorers and the fur traders began to venture west into the wilderness, they used the rivers and streams for their highways. The first roads were merely portage paths over which they carried their canoes from the end of one water route to the beginning of another. When settlers began to move west through the forests and over the Alleghenies, parties of axemen moved ahead of the wagons to cut paths through the trees and brush. Later these trails were paved by crude roads of "corduroy," or lengths of logs laid side by side to form a dry but bumpy road.

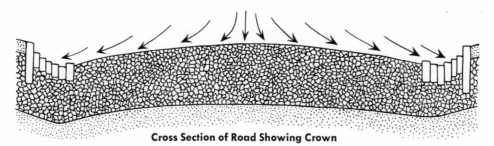

Cross Section of Road Showing Crown

Still later, the railroads served to haul goods and passengers for long distances as the West opened to permanent settlements. Crude wagon trails led from farms and ranches to the towns. Later on, rolled earth roads were a slight improvement, but these were still impassable in muddy weather.

Roads made of loose material, such as gravel or crushed oyster shells, were found to be passable in almost any kind of weather because the small particles of loose material, even when rolled down hard and flat, allowed water to drain off quickly, and kept mud from forming.

In about 1815, John McAdam, a Scottish engineer, developed the macadam road, made of crushed limestone moistened and rolled into place. Macadam roads soon were found everywhere in the United States, because they were inexpensive and easy to build. In cities and towns, the crushed limestone was often mixed with hot asphalt and provided hard-surfaced streets.

Agitation for paved streets and roads in America came from the public even before the automobile made good roads indispensable. At the time the first automobiles appeared in 1893, there were a number of bicycle clubs throughout the country whose members were urging the building of more paved roads.

Nevertheless, it was not until 1908 that the first full mile of concrete highway was built on Woodward Avenue north of Detroit, Michigan. This stretch of hard, smooth highway drew owners of automobiles from near and far for the pleasure of rolling over its concrete surface. This was not the first stretch of concrete road, however, for a street only 220 feet long had been paved in Bellefontaine, Ohio, in 1893.

Concrete is expensive, and for a number of years many roads were built of asphalt laid over a base of concrete. These asphalt roads wore out easily, however, as automobiles increased in size and speed, and as heavy trucks began to appear on the roads. The asphalt became quite soft in summer weather, and was scuffed and rutted by the

Map of Roads in United States in 1907

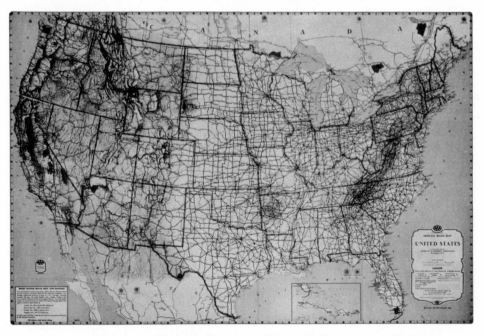

Map of Roads in United States Today

friction of tires. Today, concrete is one of the standard materials for streets and highways.

The United States has never been able to keep pace with the demand for paved streets and highways. No sooner have additional miles been laid, than traffic increases so that within a few years still more paved roads are needed. This is a field in which many civil engineers will be needed for years to come.

The building of a modern superhighway requires many big machines and men.

The building of a modern superhighway is an exciting business, requiring many men and quantities of huge machines. Moving through swamps, woods, dumping grounds, even knocking down whole residential sections in their way, bulldozers and road scrapers prepare the bed of the highway. As this work is done, hundreds of small dump trucks hurry back and forth, bringing loads of cinders and gravel to fill in the foundation of the road. They are followed by huge trucks which carry concrete-mixers, mixing the concrete on the way to the job. Pile-driving machinery is at work building bridges where the highway is to cross rivers and valleys, and creating underpasses and overpasses where one highway intersects another at different levels,

Before you graduate from engineering college, the United States will be in the middle of one of the largest highway building programs in its history. You may join more than a million men and women engaged in putting down 41,000 miles of paved highway running through 42 states and passing through 209 cities.

BUILDING IN THE MODERN AGE

Today most Americans spend the greater part of their lives inside buildings rather than out-of-doors. This is not true in most of the world, nor was it true in America a hundred years ago. During that time we have changed from a rural to an urban-dwelling population.

Even those of us who live in relatively small towns are familiar with buildings which it would not have been possible to build less than 50 years ago. Today there is no engineering limit to the height of a building. Give an engineer a good bedrock base on which to build, and enough money, materials and equipment, and he will build into the very clouds. Frank Lloyd Wright, who was one of the foremost modern architects, seriously proposed a mile-high skyscraper for the city of Chicago, and developed practical plans for the building.

Less than a hundred years ago, there were serious limits to the height of any building. For the most part, the same methods of building that had been used by the Greeks and Romans were still in effect. Arches and columns still bore the entire weight of the walls and roof of a building. Each story they were required to support meant that heavier and more numerous columns and arches had to be built. If a really tall building were going up, the base measurements of the building had to be increased almost in proportion to its height. There was no safe way to erect a tall, slim building. If there had been, such a building would have been impractical for another reason—no one would have wanted to climb the many flights of stairs necessary to live or work on the upper stories.

Today, however, buildings can be built to any height, and the height need have little relation to the width of the base. In many of our cities, buildings rise 15 or 20 stories in very narrow spaces between other buildings. They are built, often, with banks of one-suite office units on each side of an elevator shaft.

What has made the skyscraper possible? Two things, chiefly: the elevator, of course; and the steel skeleton framework which supports the entire structure.

Later, hydraulic elevators were introduced. They required a pit,

The first elevators were belt-driven machines which were run off the line shafting in the manner that was common in the 1850's. Elisha Graves Otis demonstrated the first practical passenger elevator in 1854 at the Crystal Palace in New York and made his first installation in a five-story building in New York City in 1857.

Later, hydraulic elevators were introduced. They required a pit, or cylinder, beneath a building as deep as the building was tall. When the elevator was resting at the first floor, it sat on a plunger which extended down into the pit. Water could be pumped into the pit to apply pressure which would raise the elevator. Releasing the water pressure allowed the elevator to descend. There were heavy counterweights which compensated for part of the load whether they were in motion or at rest

Realizing that a deep pit was a great disadvantage, Otis developed another elevator system which allowed its use in taller buildings. The car was suspended from cables which ran up over the drive sheave to a counterweight. The friction between these ropes and the surface of the sheave as it was rotated caused the ropes to move the car. There were cables that ran from the counterweight to the bottom of the car to compensate for the difference in length of the hoistway cables for varying positions in the hoistway so that the static load remained constant.

While hydraulic elevators are still in use today, usually powerful electric motors, assisted by counterweights, are used to operate elevators in tall skyscrapers. These elevators ascend smoothly at high speed and their passengers do not have any sensation of the speed at which they operate.

The standard type of elevator for tall buildings is the direct-traction elevator. The motors are placed at the top of the shaft. They turn a drive shaft which has a series of pulley wheels, or sheaves. The elevator cables run from the top of the elevator car up to these pulley wheels, then around them and down to the counterweight.

With the counterweight balancing the weight of the car, the electric motors do not have to support the entire weight of the car

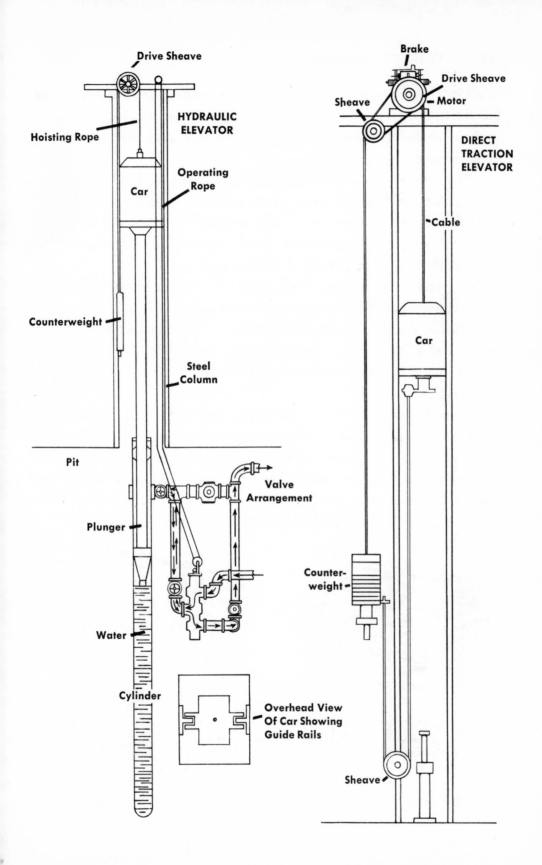

Drive Sheave

Hoisting Rope

HYDRAULIC ELEVATOR

Car

Operating Rope

Counterweight

Steel Column

Pit

Plunger

Valve Arrangement

Water

Cylinder

Overhead View Of Car Showing Guide Rails

Brake

Drive Sheave

Sheave

Motor

DIRECT TRACTION ELEVATOR

Cable

Car

Counter-weight

Sheave

to lift it. They have to raise only the *difference* between the weights of the car and the counterweight, which are always varying according to their positions in the elevator shaft and the number of passengers being carried.

The steel skeleton was even more important in the development of tall buildings. In order to fully understand just what a steel framework does for a building, let us examine one of the last big buildings built *without* a steel framework. This was the Pulitzer Building in New York City, completed in 1890. The walls of this 14-story building had to carry their own weight and support the weight of the roof. Because of the huge weight load on the walls, from roof to street level, the base walls of the Pulitzer Building had to be more than 9 feet thick! Imagine how thick the base walls of the 102-story Empire State Building would have to be today if it were built in this way!

Even before the Pulitzer Building was completed, however, a revolutionary new kind of building was going up in Chicago—the ten-story Home Insurance Company building. Although a tall building for its time, the base walls were no thicker than those at the top, and the walls were thinner than any building of its size that had thus far been built. The builder was William LeBaron Jenney.

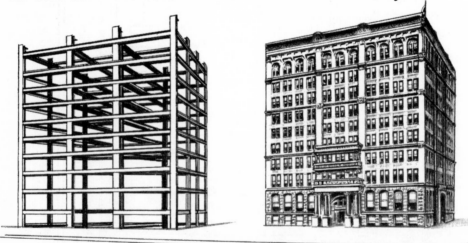

The ten-story Home Insurance Company building was the first skyscraper.

The walls of this building were not supporting any weight; they were merely enclosing the space between the real supports of the building—a framework of iron and steel! The builders started out on the lower floors with iron girders, but on the last several stories they switched to steel, which is lighter and stronger. These girders carried the whole weight of the structure down to the piers. The brick walls were merely curtains to enclose the building, which explains why such walls are commonly called *curtain walls.*

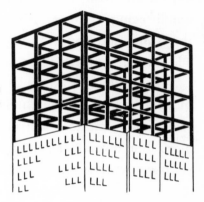

By using a steel skeleton as the framework for a building, engineers can design skyscrapers to overcome crowded conditions in many cities.

The Home Insurance Building was not as tall as some buildings that were being built according to the old method. But construction engineers were quick to see the importance of the steel frame structure.

The 14-story Tacoma Building in Chicago, completed in 1889, was the first all-steel skeleton frame building. It was the first building in which the walls were started at the top, rather than at the bottom. Engineers had discovered that, since the steel framework supported the whole weight of the building, the curtain walls could be placed wherever and whenever convenient to the building schedule. The Tacoma Building was also the first tall building in which the girders were riveted rather than bolted together. Bolts were time-consuming because they had to be tightened. They often worked loose as the building swayed under the stress of winds. Rivets could be heated red-hot, and a head pounded tight while the metal was soft. This was a fastening that would last as long as the girders themselves.

Several tall buildings had been erected in Chicago before the first building of skyscraper proportions was built in New York City. This was the Manhattan Life Insurance Building, on Broadway, opposite Trinity Church. It was the first building in which engineers used caissons, with compressed air chambers, to go down through mud and sand to bedrock. This was the same procedure used for sinking the piers of big bridges. The caissons were filled with concrete, and then topped with steel piers, on which the steel framework was begun. The New York Manhattan Life Building was the first to have windbracing—that is, crossbeams within the skeleton frame, giving the frame additional strength in the same way that truss members add strength to a bridge.

The tallest building in the world is the Empire State Building in New York City, which rises 1,250 feet from street level. This is a real monument to construction engineers. Although built in 1931, more than a quarter-century ago, the Empire State Building has not yet been exceeded in height by any other building in the world.

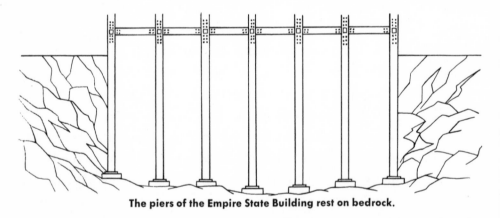

The piers of the Empire State Building rest on bedrock.

The foundation of this building is 50 feet below the street, where the piers rest on bedrock. More than 100 steel columns carry the weight of the building—totaling 365,000 tons—to the foundation. The frame has windbraces but, even with these, during storms the top of this mighty building has a measured sway of one-half inch— one-fourth inch each way from the center.

There are 102 floors in the Empire State Building, and more than

60 passenger-carrying elevators which operate at a speed of 1,000 feet per minute. It took the Egyptians generations to build the Pyramids. It took modern engineering machinery and methods only 14 months from foundation to finish to build the Empire State Building, with more than 3,500 workmen of 50 different trades employed in its construction.

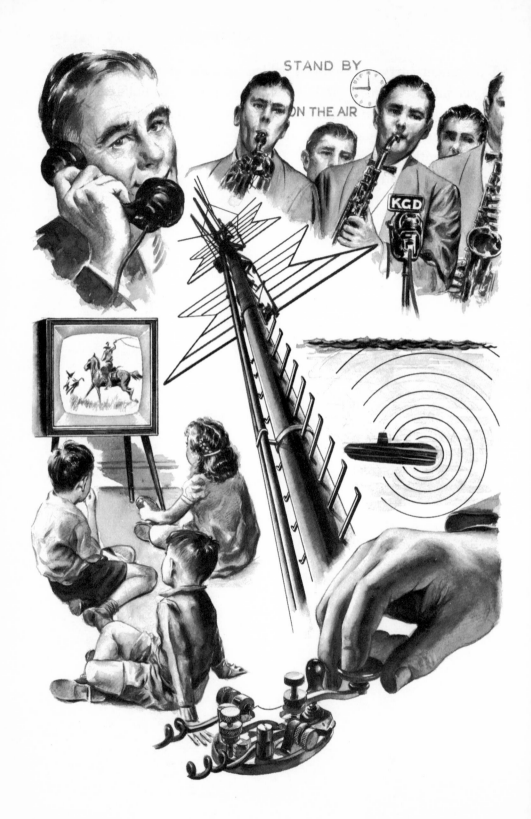

ELECTRICAL ENGINEERING

C HAPTER V discussed the way in which men discovered the principles of electromagnetism and electricity, and how they then learned that they could not only generate electricity, but also use it to operate motors.

Today, electricity plays an important part in a bewildering number of activities in everyday life. It is quite difficult to mark the limits of a special field for the electrical engineer, since the knowledge and application of electrical principles are used in so many other fields of engineering.

The civil engineer, certainly, would have a hard time operating without the help of the many electrical controls and devices used in construction and in the operation of such projects as bridges, canal locks and the like. The automobile is powered by a gasoline engine, and yet the modern automobile could not operate without its electrically operated starter and generator; nor could it have its power steering and power braking mechanisms, its lights and turn signals, or its electrical timing system. Railroads and other public transportation facilities could not maintain safe schedules without the electrically

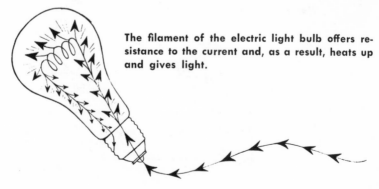

The filament of the electric light bulb offers resistance to the current and, as a result, heats up and gives light.

operated lights, switches and signal systems which are so much a part of the over-all operation of such systems. We call our newest ships and submarines atomic-powered, and yet the atomic energy generated is used only to provide the heat which creates steam to operate turbine generators. These generate electricity to operate the electric motors which actually drive these ships and subs.

The exactly calculated and controlled resistance of certain metals and materials to electric current has been put to use quite cleverly to produce many modern wonders. The resistance to current of the filament inside an electric light bulb, for instance, produces the brilliant glow of light we have come to take as a matter of course. It is the calculated resistance of certain elements to electric current that produces heat in the electric oven and in other appliances: the electric toaster, the iron, the clothes dryer, electric blankets and other resistance devices. Count the electric motors in your house: the blower on the furnace system; the fans or the air conditioner; the electric refrigerator; the electric clocks; the sewing machine; the vacuum cleaner; the portable electric tools in your dad's workshop. Count the make-and-break circuit devices in your home: the doorbell circuit; the automatic thermostat controlling the operation of the furnace; the automatic alarm system on your clock radio. Don't forget the electrical devices of communication, either—the telephone, radio and television set. Our homes are whirring with electrical

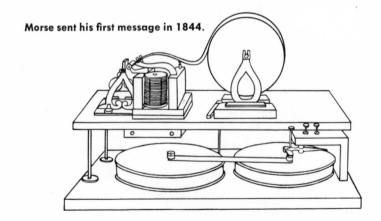

Morse sent his first message in 1844.

devices, quite sharply in contrast to the candlelit, coal-heated homes of our grandfathers' parents, who lived, after all, not so very long ago.

Communications is the biggest subdivision in the big field of electrical engineering. If we examine this field as fully as we can, we shall have a good understanding of the whole field.

The *telegraph system* was regarded as a scientific marvel when Samuel F. B. Morse sent his first code message over a wire between Washington, D.C., and Baltimore in 1844. Yet the principle of the telegraph is simplicity itself—as Morse discovered. Tapping sounds could be made at any desired interval by making and breaking an electric current conducted along a wire ending in an electromagnet which would attract or repel a free bar of conductive metal. This was a principle that had been understood thoroughly many years before Morse began his experiments — his real contribution was in the development of an electric relay which would enable a current to be sent over a long distance. Morse's relay was a series of battery-operated circuits—when the circuit was closed on the first battery, the electrical impulse closed the circuit next down the line, and so on, so that the signal arrived at the other end after being transmitted from one relay to another. Relay systems are used today, but generator units are used instead of batteries to pass the impulses along.

It is difficult for us, accustomed as we are to the speed of telephone, radio and television communications, to appreciate what the telegraph meant as an invention in the 1800's. To people accustomed to depend on the mails which sometimes took weeks to deliver news and business information, the telegraph was a miracle. Telegraph poles bearing wires soon crisscrossed the nation, and newspapers from one end of the country to the other could receive news almost as soon as it happened. Telegraph lines followed the railroads, and orders to the train crew flashed ahead of the speeding train to a station down the line. Stock market quotations in New York could reach San Francisco brokers on the same day. Business firms received rush orders and other vital information in time to meet the emergency needs of their customers.

INTERNATIONAL CODE

1 • — — — —	• — A	— • • • B	— • — • C	— • • D
2 • • — — —	• E	• • — • F	— — • G	• • • • H
3 • • • — —	• • I	• — — — J	— • — K	• — • • L
4 • • • • —	— — M	— • N	— — — O	• — — • P
5 • • • • •	— — • — Q	• — • R	• • • S	— T
6 — • • • •	• • — U	• • • — V	• — — W	— • • — X
7 — — • • •		— • — — Y	— — • • Z	
8 — — — • •				
9 — — — — •				
0 — — — — —				

. • — • — • —	
? • • — — • •	
! — — • • — —	
Call • — • —	
Finish • — • — •	
Wait • — • • •	
Understand • • • — •	
Don't Understand — • • • • — •	

Morse invented a simple dot-dash code to make his telegraph system communicate symbols that could be translated back into words. The telegraph operator became a highly skilled, highly paid employee of newspapers and news services, railroads, stock exchange firms and private business houses with branches in many cities. In addition to the Morse code, they developed a sort of telegraphic shorthand of their own, called the Phillips code, which speeded the transmission of messages. In the newsroom of a Washington, D. C., news service, operators would flick the handles of their sending keys, called "bugs," and send a rapid staccato of dots and dashes to newspaper offices all over the country. In these newspaper offices, receiving operators would sit beside sounder boxes, translating the dots and dashes in their minds, and typing out the translated words. The signals they received were not complete words, but abbreviations of words in the Phillips code. For instance, a receiving operator might hear on his sounder a story which started like this:

"WX—T SCOTUS TDY UPHLD . . ."

But the story the operator typed for the newspaper would start like this:

"Washington, D. C.—The Supreme Court of the United States today upheld . . ."

As may be seen from this example, the Phillips code was made up of abbreviations largely using key consonant letters of the alphabet, leaving out most of the vowels and many of the consonants which were not necessary to the understanding of a word or a phrase.

One thing leads to another in the engineering field. To get his telegraph lines across New York Harbor, Morse laid rubber-covered cables on the bottom of the harbor. By 1850, six years after the invention of the telegraph, undersea cables strung across the floor of the English Channel were carrying messages between England and France. Ships began attempting to unreel cable across the Atlantic in 1856, but there were many failures because the cables kept breaking. Not until 1858 was the first complete cable laid across the bed of the Atlantic over the shortest distance, between Ireland and Newfoundland. That was the beginning of rapid international communications.

Today there are 20 telegraph and telephone cables across the Atlantic. Each cable is composed of a number of wires, and each wire can transmit a number of separate messages at the same time.

But the telegraph operator and the Morse code are rarities today. They have been supplanted by a machine—the teletype, or teleprinter — which transmits electrical impulses and translates them into a written message at the receiving end. Only one operator is required, at the sending end. He or she types out the message on a machine with a standard typewriter keyboard. Some machines transmit the impulses directly—that is to say, when a key is punched in New York, the cor-

Pressing the sending key at your house closes the circuit and sends current flowing, which causes the iron nails at the receiving set to become electromagnets. They draw down the strip of iron to strike the nailheads with a sharp click.

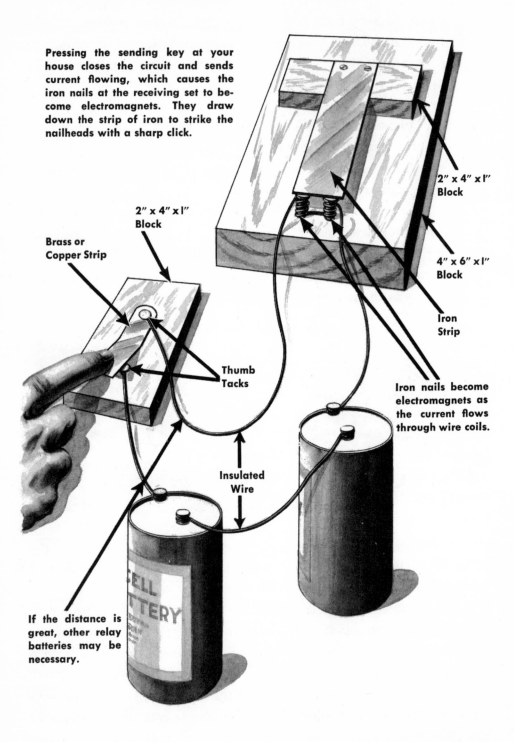

2" x 4" x1" Block

Brass or Copper Strip

2" x 4" x1" Block

Thumb Tacks

2" x 4" x1" Block

4" x 6" x1" Block

Iron Strip

Iron nails become electromagnets as the current flows through wire coils.

Insulated Wire

If the distance is great, other relay batteries may be necessary.

CELL BATTERY

responding letter appears on the receiving machine in San Francisco. For smoother operation, however, most teletype sending machines punch the message onto a tape by means of a series of coded holes. This tape is then fed into a sending machine. The transmission of the message can be speeded up by the use of the tape. For instance, it is rarely possible for the human sender to exceed 80 words per minute for more than a very short period of work. But the tape can be fed through a machine and received at the other end as fast as a thousand words per minute. This means that the work of a dozen operators can be sent over a busy teletype circuit in the same time it would take one of them to transmit a single message.

In addition to taking the place of the old-time telegrapher and his key and sounder, the teletype machine is used to operate linotype machines for the setting of printing type. Thus, newspapers and news magazines can receive their stories and have them set into type at the same time.

Your own telegraph system. You might like to make your own telegraph system, so that you can send secret messages in code to a pal who lives next door. Such a telegraph system is easy to build, and does not require a great deal of material.

For each sending and receiving set at either end of the line you will need a flat piece of wood measuring about 4 by 6 inches; a small block of wood measuring about 2 by 4 inches; a thin strip of iron about 4 inches long and 2 inches wide; a flexible piece of brass or copper about 1 inch wide and 3 inches long; two dry cell batteries; enough insulated wire to reach from your house to the house next door and back again; two iron nails; and two thumbtacks. That is not a lot of material when you consider you're going to wind up with a telegraph system.

The drawing on the opposite page shows how the telegraph set is assembled much more clearly than it could be explained in words alone. Notice particularly how the batteries are connected. This must be done exactly as in the drawing, or your electrical circuit will not be completed.

The strip of brass or copper is the sending key. When the key is in contact with the thumbtack underneath, the circuit is closed, and the strip of iron is pulled down to the iron nail. This is because the iron nail has been turned into an electromagnet by the coil of copper wire wound around it. Only when current is flowing through the wire does the nail become an electromagnet.

To operate your home telegraph system, you merely have to tap the sending key to form dots and dashes. Each time the key is pressed down against the thumbtack and allowed to spring back up again, a click-clack sound is created by the iron strip striking the magnetized nail and springing back up. You will learn, with practice, how to make the dots and dashes of Morse code and how to receive them from your friends at the other end.

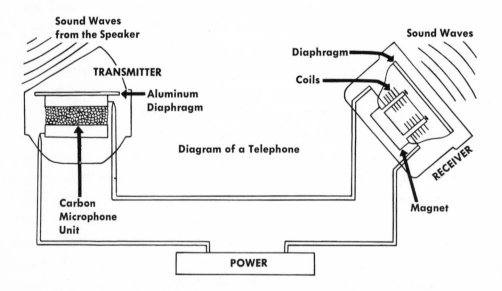

The telegraph, while in wide use for specialized communication such as we have described, is not nearly as important today as it was in the 1800's. That is because the burden of rapid communication is shared by another device which depends upon electricity for its operation—the telephone.

The *telephone,* first demonstrated successfully by Alexander Graham Bell in 1876, was a vast improvement over telegraphy because it permitted sound waves set up by the human voice to be projected over a wire from one instrument to another.

The principle of the telephone is very simple. When you speak into a telephone mouthpiece, the sound waves set up by your voice cause vibrations in a thin metal plate, or diaphragm. Behind this diaphragm is a small box containing fine grains of carbon. The vibrations of the diaphragm, set up by the sound waves of your voice, exert pressure on the carbon granules. This pressure varies with the tones and modulations of your words. As the carbon granules are pressed together and released under various degrees of pressure, they exert a varying degree of resistance to the electric current that is flowing through the carbon mass. More current flows when the carbon particles are pressed tightly together; less current flows when the particles are farther apart. These changes in the degree of resistance to the current passing through the carbon mean that the strength of the current is constantly being varied so long as you are speaking. The current, always changing in strength, passes through a connecting wire to the receiver of the other telephone. There the current affects the receiver through an electromagnet and another diaphragm similar to that in the mouthpiece. The changes in current strength coming over the wire from the mouthpiece affect the electromagnet, causing it to vibrate in the same pattern and setting up vibrations in the receiving diaphragm which cause sound waves duplicating the words you speak into the telephone mouthpiece.

Remember, it is not your voice that the telephone transmits. The sound waves are turned into electric current of varying strength and finally back into sound waves again. You have a "telephone voice," that is, your voice sounds differently over a telephone than your voice sounds in a room, but it is close enough to your actual voice so that anyone who talks to you frequently on the telephone is able to identify your voice.

This is the simple principle of the telephone. The actual transmission of telephone messages, through complex switchboards from one telephone company exchange to another and over long distance wires, is a much more complicated matter involving the use of nearly all the electronic devices that man has been able to invent.

A multiple switchboard serving 6,000 subscribers has connections for the lines of every single subscriber. Each of these connection points can be connected to any one of the other subscribers' connection points. This is made possible within the reach of each operator by repeating the appearance of each customer's line every few feet along the face of the switchboard. This arrangement is called "switchboard multiple." Each multiple appearance of all 6,000 numbers is a switchboard multiple section. Such a board might have 20 multiple sections, which would mean 120,000 points of connection are required on the switchboard.

Telephone wires carry most telephone messages throughout the world. But since electrical impulses can also be carried by telegraph cable and by radio waves, both are often used in combination with the telephone. The wireless telephone enables conversations to take place between airports and pilots of airplanes in flight; between station dispatchers and the conductors and engineers of passenger trains speeding over the rails; and between shore connections and ships at sea. In the same way, the undersea cables which used to transmit only telegraph messages are used today to carry telephone conversations from one continent to another, so that businessmen may telephone their foreign branches, or the President of the United States may pick up a telephone in the White House to ask an important question of the Prime Minister of Great Britain in London.

The telephone industry makes use of the services of a large number of different kinds of engineers. Electrical engineers, of course, are needed to make all sorts of installations and to solve all kinds of problems for telephone companies. In addition, civil engineers and construction engineers are required in building telephone exchanges, laying underground and overhead telephone wires, and solving the many physical problems encountered in providing telephone service to the nation.

You could make and install a private telephone system inside

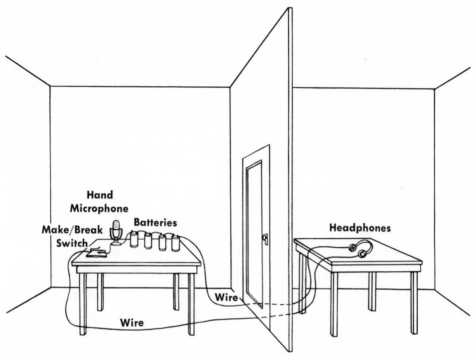

BUILD YOUR OWN TELEPHONE SET

your house, or between your house and that of a nearby pal. It would be complicated and expensive to do so with conventional-type telephone instruments, however. A system which is a real telephone line, but which uses inexpensive radio earphones and carbon hand microphones (such as are used in public announcement systems) will be fairly easy to construct.

You can get all the materials needed at any radio supply house: the two hand mikes, the radio earphones, four No. 6 dry cell batteries, the wire, four terminal points, two make-and-break switches and a relay which will be required if your line is more than 100 feet long.

The wiring diagram shown above will enable you to set up one transmitting-receiving unit. Two of these units will have to be set up for a two-way conversation, of course. If your practical experience with electricity is not sufficient for you to follow the diagram, any experienced adult can help you with it.

The *radio* opened up a new world of communication. When perfected, it was possible to transmit sound in all its infinite variety to any part of the world, and, in the future, when men from earth reach other planets, we shall communicate with them by radio.

In its beginnings, radio was as crude as most inventions usually are at birth. It became possible in 1887, when Heinrich Hertz discovered how to produce and detect electromagnetic waves, now called *hertzian waves*, or radio waves. A number of scientists immediately recognized the possibility of sending telegraphic messages by means of hertzian waves. But they ran into many practical problems in their experiments. Nevertheless, they did set up the framework in which radio could at least theoretically be expected to operate—the creation and transmission of hertzian waves by means of an *oscillator*, and the receiving and the recording of them by means of a *detector*.

Building on various crude devices of earlier experimenters, Guglielmo Marconi, a young Italian inventor, began working toward a practical method of wireless transmission in 1894. By causing an electric current to jump a spark gap, Marconi could set up oscillating hertzian waves in a dot-dash pattern similar to telegraph signals. At the receiving end, the signals were picked up by a detector, called a *coherer*, which was made of a tube of iron filings. Hertzian waves captured in the receiver decreased the resistance of the iron filings, which bunched together, or *cohered*. A mechanical device was used

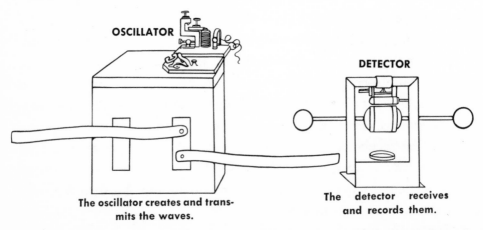

OSCILLATOR

DETECTOR

The oscillator creates and transmits the waves.

The detector receives and records them.

The radio became possible after Heinrich Hertz discovered how to produce and detect electromagnetic waves.

to tap the coherer at regular intervals to loosen the filings again so the coherer could continue to receive signals.

Marconi hit upon the aerial as a means for improving the transmission and reception of his *wireless telegraph*, as radio was first called. In 1896 he sent a message nearly two miles, and soon afterward had improved this distance to eight miles. In 1901 he sent a historic signal, the letter "S," from England to Newfoundland, the first message to travel across the Atlantic by radio.

Radio waves are only one of six classes of electromagnetic waves, which include heat and light waves. Radio waves are long waves— that is to say, the *frequency* with which they go from trough to crest and back again is long, compared to other electromagnetic waves. Radio waves range from one-tenth of an inch to several miles in length, and their wave frequencies range from 10,000 to 30,000,000 cycles per second. You can see that there is a wide range of radio waves, even though they belong to a particular class of long electromagnetic waves. Radio waves are all long waves of low frequency, even though the terms *ultra-short waves* and *high frequency* are used to describe certain radio wave bands.

When a radio transmitter sends out waves, they travel in all directions. Thus radio receivers can detect these waves to the north, south, east and west of the transmitter. These waves will also penetrate to mines underground or to planes high above the transmitter. When radio waves strike the aerial of a receiver, they set up a small

THE ELECTROMAGNETIC SPECTRUM

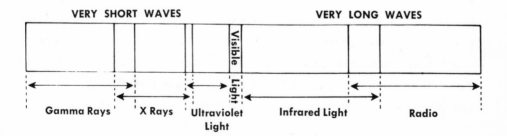

current in the aerial that is like the current that produced the waves at the transmitter. This small current goes to a detector tube which, in effect, separates an audio signal from the radio carrier wave. The audio signal is amplified and sent to the loudspeaker where it reproduces the voices and sounds that were broadcast from the transmitter.

A whole book would be required to trace the step-by-step development of radio from the simple stage of wireless telegraphy, as Marconi developed it, to radio as we know it today. One part, for instance the detector tube, began as a flask of iron filings, went through many stages until it merged first as the vacuum tube and finally as the electronic transistor in use today to detect signals.

The smallest radio set in your house is a complicated electronic system compared to the basic system of radio we shall explain here. Nevertheless, a transmitter and receiver are still basic parts of any radio communication, just as they were in Marconi's day.

Radio as we know it is a combination of the wireless telegraph and the telephone. In the broadcasting station, the words or notes of music are picked up by the sensitive diaphragm of a microphone. This is very similar to the mouthpiece of a telephone. As the diaphragm of the microphone vibrates in response to the sound waves which strike it from the voice of the announcer or singer, corresponding pulsations are set up in the weak direct current which passes through the microphone. This current, which becomes an electric pattern of sound, goes to an amplifier—an electronic tube which strengthens the current.

Thus far in the broadcasting, the sound pattern has been imprinted only on an electric current. No hertzian, or radio, waves are involved. But in the next step, the current passes through a *modulator*. This takes the sound pattern from the current and imprints it on radio waves which have been set up by a generator which, in radio, is called an oscillator tube. The radio waves are strengthened, or amplified, as they move up to the antenna of the broadcasting station, from which they are broadcast to all points of the compass.

Let us go back to the second step in radio broadcasting—an important one called *modulation*. There are two kinds of modulation—amplitude modulation and frequency modulation, or AM and FM radio. AM radio is the kind we have explained, in which the strength, or amplitude, of the radio waves is varied as the signals are sent out. In FM radio, the frequency of the radio waves is varied, instead of the amplitude. There are two important differences between the two systems which make each suitable for special jobs. The AM radio signals are very powerful, and can be transmitted over long distances. But the long waves of AM radio take up a lot of room in the frequency ranges available, so that only a limited number of AM radio stations are possible in a given area. FM radio waves, on the other hand, are ultra-short (this system is often called short-wave radio), and many more stations can broadcast in the same relative area. Also, FM radio signals are less subject to static (magnetic disturbances), and they produce clearer, more faithful reproductions of the original sounds.

The heart of a radio receiver is its variable condenser, which allows the set to be tuned in to the wave length of a particular broadcasting station. Without this, the radio listener would not be able to select stations from the entire wave band available to either AM or FM radio. When the variable condenser is set to catch signals of a

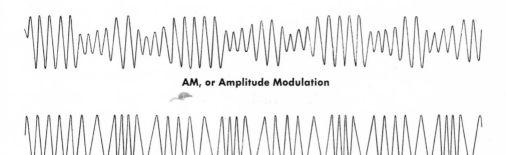

AM, or Amplitude Modulation

FM, or Frequency Modulation

certain wavelength, and a station is broadcasting, the radio waves from the sending station set up alternating impulses of the same frequency in the receiver's antenna. These impulses are passed from the antenna to radio frequency tubes which amplify, or strengthen, the signals. The signals then enter the detector tube, which rectifies them—that is, it changes the alternating impulses from the antenna to a direct current, which vibrates in the same pattern as the original sound waves that started from the broadcasting station. This current is amplified, or strengthened, and then enters the radio loudspeaker. Here it is reproduced as sound by means of an electromagnet and a diaphragm, working on the same principle as the telephone receiver. The broadcast cycle is then complete. All this complicated variation of patterns and currents takes place within a fraction of a second, nevertheless, so that a violinist's bow is scarcely drawn over the strings before you hear the note in your home hundreds of miles away; and when the announcer looks at the studio clock and gives the correct time, it will be the same on your living room clock, if your clock is running correctly.

Your own receiver. The beginner cannot obtain a clear understanding of radio without actually building a basic circuit. Today the field of electronics has reached a point where television, guided missiles, automatic calculators, etc., have become a part of our everyday language. Yet even the most complicated electronic equipment still requires the use of some basic circuits which, though improved, have been in use since the beginnings of radio.

The best starting point for a junior experimenter is a crystal set. Unlike other types of radio receivers, a crystal set uses no batteries, nor need it be plugged into the household electrical circuit. The sound that is heard in the earphones used with a crystal set is obtained entirely from the radio energy picked up by the antenna.

The crystal receiver shown in the illustrations and diagrams here is quite simple to make. The entire set is built upon a base of ¼-inch-thick plywood measuring 6⅜ by 8½ inches. All of the parts, wires

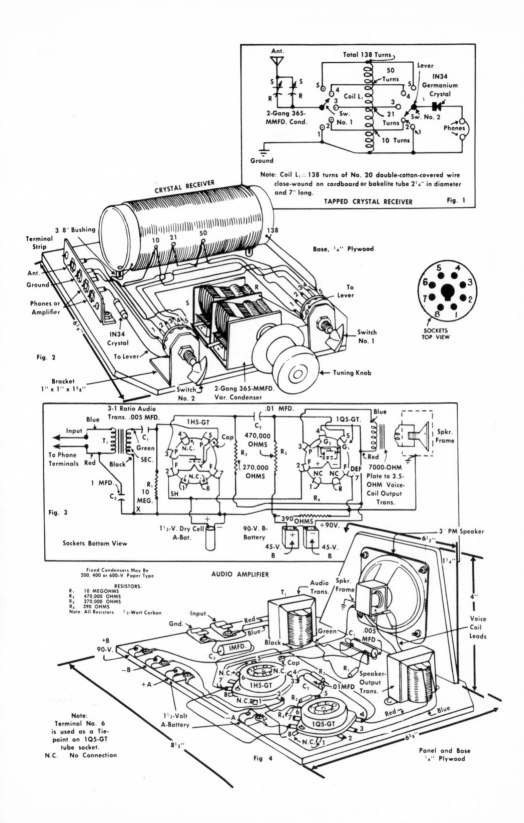

Ant.

Total 138 Turns

50 Turns

Lever

IN34 Germanium Crystal

Coil L₁

21 Turns

10 Turns

2-Gang 365-MMFD. Cond.

Sw. No. 1

Sw. No. 2

Phones

Ground

Note: Coil L₁ = 138 turns of No. 20 double-cotton-covered wire close-wound on cardboard or bakelite tube 2¼" in diameter and 7" long.

TAPPED CRYSTAL RECEIVER

Fig. 1

CRYSTAL RECEIVER

3 8" Bushing

Terminal Strip

Ant.

Ground

Phones or Amplifier

IN34 Crystal

Fig. 2

To Lever

Bracket 1" x 1" x 1⅝"

Switch No. 2

2-Gang 365-MMFD. Var. Condenser

Base, ¼" Plywood

To Lever

Switch No. 1

Tuning Knob

SOCKETS TOP VIEW

3-1 Ratio Audio Trans. .005 MFD.

Blue

Input

To Phone Terminals

Red

Black

Green

SEC.

1 MFD.

Fig. 3

Sockets Bottom View

.01 MFD.

1H5-GT

C₂

470,000 OHMS

R₂

270,000 OHMS

R₁ 10 MEG. X

SH

1½-V. Dry Cell A-Bat.

390 OHMS

90-V. B-Battery

45-V. B

45-V. B

1Q5-GT.

Blue

Red

R₄

+90V.

7000-OHM Plate to 3.5-OHM Voice-Coil Output Trans.

Spkr. Frame

3" PM Speaker

6½"

1¼"

4"

Voice Coil Leads

Fixed Condensers May Be 200, 400 or 600-V. Paper Type

RESISTORS:
R₁ 10 MEGOHMS
R₂ 470,000 OHMS
R₃ 270,000 OHMS
R₄ 390 OHMS

Note: All Resistors ½-Watt Carbon

AUDIO AMPLIFIER

Audio Trans.

Spkr. Frame

Gnd.

Input

Red

Blue

Black

Green

C₁ .005 MFD

+B 90-V.

−B

+A

C₃ 1MFD.

N.C.

Cap

N.C.

C₄

1H5-GT

C₂ .01MFD

R₃

R₁

Speaker-Output Trans.

Red

Blue

Note: Terminal No. 6 is used as a Tie-point on 1Q5-GT tube socket.

N.C. No Connection

8½"

1½-Volt A-Battery

−A

R₂

R₄

1Q5-GT

N.C.

Fig 4

6⅜"

Panel and Base ¼" Plywood

and connections may be obtained from a radio-supply house—either one located near you, or one from which you can order by mail.

These are the things you must order:

One Bakelite or heavy cardboard tube, 2¼ inches in diameter and 7 inches long.
One small spool of No. 20 magnet wire, double cotton covered.
One Sylvania 1N34 germanium crystal.
Two single-pole, five-position switches.
One terminal strip with four insulated lugs.
One two-gang 365-mmfd. variable condenser.
One tuning knob.
Two pointer knobs.
Two ⅝-inch bushings.
Two angle brackets, 1 by 1 by 1⅝ inches, for mounting switches.
Eleven flathead machine screws, No. 6-32, ½-inch long.
Eleven hex nuts to fit above screws.
75 feet of antenna wire.
Four rubber bumper feet with No. 6-32 screws.
Several lengths each of red, blue, green and black "spaghetti" (hollow tubing which serves to identify connection wires by color). See illustration on preceding page.
The wooden base on which you will mount these parts may be cut from any scrap piece of plywood, or any other kind of wood if plywood is not available.

Your first job in making the radio receiver will be to wind *exactly* 138 turns of the cotton-covered wire tightly and neatly around the coil tube. When the coil is completed, you will have to make soldered connections to the 10th, 21st and 50th turns of the coil. As you wind, therefore, place a toothpick under the 10th, 21st and 50th turns. This will leave those coils loose enough for you to slip beneath them the ends of the wires you are going to solder to those turns later.

When you have the coil wound, you mount it to the wooden base with the screws and bushings, as shown in the drawing, Fig. 2. That drawing and the diagrams with Figs. 1 and 3, will also show you how to install and connect the other parts more clearly than words could explain. If you do not know how to solder electrical connections, get some friend who does know to show you how.

After your radio receiver is assembled and connected, you cannot expect it to work until you have connected it to an aerial and a ground.

The aerial wire is strung outside, as high as you can install it between two convenient points, such as the peaks of your house roof and the roof of the garage. Insulated knobs or rings should be used at all such points of connection so that radio waves will not ground themselves before reaching the receiver. The ground wire should lead from the ground terminal of the terminal strip of the radio to any convenient cold-water pipe in your house.

With your set assembled and connected properly, and with earphones plugged in at the proper terminals, you are ready to find a station broadcasting in your vicinity. The crystal detector unit is adjustable, and you work with this until you find a sensitive spot which will cause a faint pop or crackle in the earphones. Then you move the tuning arm of the variable condenser until you hear a radio broadcast.

Later on, to gain experience with vacuum tubes and with batteries as a power source, you may want to hook an audio-amplifier system to your crystal set so that you may discard the earphones and listen to broadcasts through a loudspeaker. You should not find it difficult to make the audio-amplifier by following the diagram and sketch (Figs. 3 and 4). To connect the amplifier unit to your crystal set, you simply run wires from the terminals which formerly connected with the earphones to the input and ground clips shown in Fig. 4.

You will need to order, mount and connect the following parts for your audio-amplifier:

One 3-inch permanent magnet loudspeaker in metal frame.
Two 45-volt B batteries.
One 1½-volt A battery.
Two amplifier tubes, one 1H5-GT, one 1Q5-GT.
Three 400-volt, paper-type fixed condensers, one .005 mfd., one .01 mfd., and one .1 mfd.
Four ½-watt carbon resistors, one 10 megohms, one 470,000 ohms, one 270,000 ohms, and one 390 ohms.
One unshielded-type audio transformer of 3-to-1 or 3½-to-1 ratio, single-grid-to-single-plate construction.
One output transformer, with 7000-ohm plate, 3.5 ohm voice coil.

Two octal, above-chassis tube sockets.
One tie-point strip with two insulated lugs.
Seven No. 6 soldering lugs.
Four No. 6-32 ornamental-head screws.
Four No. 6-32, ¼-inch hex nuts.
Eleven No. 6 gimlet-point, ¼-inch self-tapping screws.
Four No. 6 gimlet-point self-tapping screws, ½-inch.
Three No. 6 gimlet-point, self-tapping screws, ⅜-inch.
Four rubber bumper feet, with No. 6-32 screws.
As a framework on which to mount and connect these parts, you will
need to make the plywood base and speaker baffle shown in Fig. 4.

The converting of your crystal set from headphone reception to loudspeaker reproduction of the sounds is done by means of the two amplifying tubes, which are examples of the electron tube.

The electron tube is a key piece of equipment in the vast and complicated engineering field called electronics. In fact, electronics has been defined as the science of producing and controlling electrons

HOW ELECTRON TUBES WORK

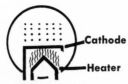
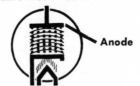

In a gas-filled tube the heater heats the cathode which gives off electrons.

When positive voltage is applied to anode it attracts billions of electrons that are "boiled" off cathode; current then flows through tube.

When anode is negatively charged it cannot attract electrons.

WHAT THE GRID (CONTROL ELECTRODE) DOES

When a certain amount of negatively charged voltage is applied to the grid, electrons cannot reach anode.

When negative voltage is reduced, electrons flow to the anode.

Flow stops when anode voltage becomes negative; then cycle repeats.

by means of electron tubes. Stated simply, the electron tube passes current through a vacuum space inside the tube by means of a flow of electrons from a filament. The radio signal is received by the outside aerial, and then is transformed into a weak electromagnetic current by means of the coil which you wound around the cardboard tube.

This weak current is amplified by the batteries and transformers before it enters the electron tubes. The current flows through these tubes as electrons. At one instant, the grid of the tube will have too many electrons, at the next instant, too few. When too few electrons are on the grid, others are drawn instantly from the filament. When too many electrons are on the grid, the escape of electrons from the filament is slowed up. These variations in the electron tube cause corresponding movements in the loudspeaker diaphragm, and this sets up corresponding vibrations in the surrounding air. Our ears pick up these variations in our own sensitive diaphragms which we call eardrums. Thus are sound waves converted into radio waves, and radio waves converted into pulsating electrical current, and this current into a varying flow of electrons, and this flow of electrons back into sound waves so faithfully reproduced that we can instantly identify the voice of a famous man as soon as we hear it on the radio or television.

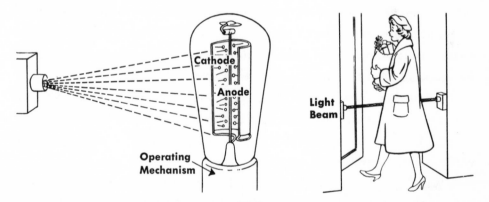

When light strikes the light-sensitive cathode, electrons flow to the anode. When the light rays are stopped, the electron flow within the tube also stops which makes the operating mechanism work.

You may have been mystified as you walked toward the doors of a modern supermarket to find that they swung open as if by magic just before you reached them. This apparent miracle is made possible by electron tubes that are sensitive to light.

These electron tubes, often called photoelectric cells, contain a thin film of light-sensitive metal, such as potassium or cesium, through which flows a negative electric current. In the center of the tube is a positively charged plate or wire loop. A current is set up when light strikes the sensitive metal, causing electrons to flow from the negative metal to the positive plate or loop.

In the case of the supermarket doors, the doors are held closed so long as a beam of light from one side of the entry strikes a vacuum tube on the other side. As you walk toward the doors, you break the beam of light with your body, and the doors spring open.

Light-sensitive electron tubes like this also set off burglar alarms when a light beam is broken by the body of a trespasser (also, unfortunately for the police and watchmen who have to answer false alarms, the beams may be broken and the alarms set off by birds, small animals, or pieces of paper blowing in the wind).

Electron tubes sensitive to light, to heat, or to various strengths of electric current are used to operate many automatic machines, calculators, camera exposure meters, guided missiles of modern warfare and many other electronic devices. Today the electronics engineer has a whole complicated field all to himself, with infinite possibilities for making useful contributions to society.

Television. Nowhere is the electron tube more important than in that field of communications and entertainment we call television, a word formed of the Greek *tele,* meaning "far off," and the Latin verb, *video,* meaning "to see."

What do we see on television? Not as faithful a reproduction of a scene as we get in the reproduction of sound over the same television set, or by radio or telephone. What we see on television is a series of still pictures transmitted to us at the rate of 30 pictures per second— so fast that our eyes complete the illusion of an actor walking, or a dancer dancing, or a horse galloping through the Badlands.

The starting point of a television picture is the camera. But this is a strange camera in which there is no film, nor any other permanent record of the scene which can be looked at again and again. Instead, a scene is pictured, sent over the air waves, registered on the screens of all receivers tuned to it, and then replaced with the next scene at the rate of 30 scenes per second.

Instead of being recorded on a film negative, the television picture is transformed into electrical energy which is transmitted to the receiving sets either through space or through a combination of space and coaxial cables which serve as relays over long distances.

The scanning beam makes a complete picture of 525 lines in one-thirtieth of a second!

The television camera does not take its pictures in one big gulp, as an ordinary camera catches a scene on film. Instead the TV camera traces, or scans, each picture in a series of lines from top to bottom —525 of these horizontal lines to each picture. The TV camera does this with lightning speed—tracing 525 lines for each picture at the rate of 30 pictures per second means 15,750 lines per second! But nevertheless, the actual procedure is a line at a time. If you look closely at the screen of your television set, you can actually see the horizontal lines in the picture which duplicate the scanning lines of the television camera in bringing the scene to your vision.

Television waves—that is, those which carry the picture part of the television broadcast—are very short radio waves. Because they are short, they oscillate from peak to valley with great frequency. Television engineers speak of these waves as high frequency waves and have divided them into two groups—VHF, or *very high frequency*, and UHF, or *ultra-high frequency*. VHF waves carry the standard commercial television broadcasts, while UHF waves carry the educational television broadcasts.

As the television camera scans the lines of its scene in ⅓₀th of a second, it transmits the scene as electrical energy which varies according to the "colors" of the picture being broadcast. In a black-and-white television picture, there are of course hundreds of shades of gray in between the absolute whites and the absolute blacks of the picture. To transmit all these shades requires a broad band width for the television station—broad enough to carry this wide range of picture signals and also to carry the wide range of sounds. In sound, for example, not many cycles of electrical energy would be necessary to carry the single note of a flute. But to transmit all the notes, overtones and harmonics in the music of a symphony orchestra requires a wide band of radio frequencies.

The electrical energy which makes up the television picture is

COMPARISON OF FREQUENCIES

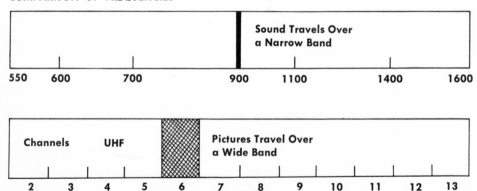

Television signals are sent out on high-frequency radio waves that occupy a band six mega-cycles wide because high frequencies are almost static free and have little other interferences. Lower frequencies are used by standard radio waves.

imposed upon a very short radio wave and sent out from the transmitting antenna. Unlike true radio waves, which spread in all directions and pass through and around most objects, the television waves
are partly blocked by the hills, buildings and other objects that stand
in the way. They are blocked entirely by the curvature of the earth.
Television transmitting antennae, therefore, must be put on the highest
buildings in town, and the range of television signals is limited to

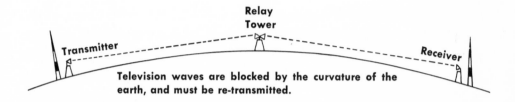

Relay
Tower

Transmitter

Receiver

Television waves are blocked by the curvature of the
earth, and must be re-transmitted.

approximately 100 miles for direct transmission. The use of relay
stations, with tall towers and coaxial cables, enables television programs to be relayed across the continent.

When television signals hit your TV antenna, the signals are
carried down to the set by the lead-in wire that runs from the roof
to the set. Both sound and picture signals travel together through the
tuner and then through amplifiers to make the signals stronger. The
sound and picture signals are separated, the sound signal being fed
to the loudspeaker and the picture signal to an electron beam which

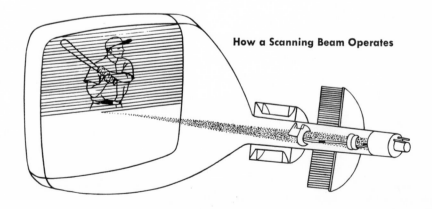

How a Scanning Beam Operates

scans the picture tube and "paints" the picture on the face of the tube by means of the 525-line scanning pattern by which the picture was transmitted from the broadcasting station in the first place.

This scanning beam moves across the picture tube "in step" with the scanning beam in the camera at the studio that is taking the televised scene. The picture tube is coated with a substance that glows in greater or lesser degree according to the number of the electrons bombarding the coating. The greater number of electrons makes the white parts of the picture, and the fewer makes the black.

This is an oversimplified explanation, of course, of how a television receiver works. There are various important intermediate steps, such as the building up of the sound and picture signals, and the focusing of the electrons into a sharp image on the picture screen. You will want to do some additional reading in books devoted entirely to television if you are interested in having a detailed understanding of the subject.

Color TV signals are the same as those in black-and-white. But instead of one picture signal riding the radio waves with the sound, there are *three* picture signals. Each of these three picture signals carries the tonal values for one of these single colors—red, green and blue. These are the primary colors of television, unlike the red, yellow and blue we know as the primary colors in painting and printing.

The red signal, for instance, will carry values of red ranging from the deepest red to the palest pink, just as the black and white

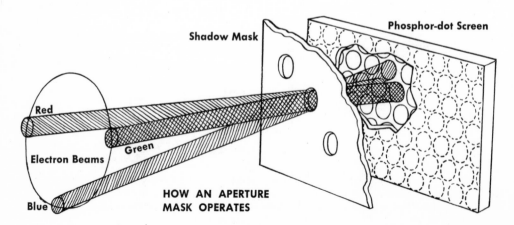

Shadow Mask

Phosphor-dot Screen

Red

Green

Electron Beams

Blue

HOW AN APERTURE
MASK OPERATES

signal ranges from deepest black to very light grays and pure white. The intensity of the color signal is determined by the strength of the current, which in turn is translated into a varying number of electrons striking the face of the picture tube.

The three color signals, although riding the same radio wavelength along with the sound, enter the television receiver separately. In the receiver, the separate beams pass through a mask filled with holes, called an aperture mask, and are converged on the face of the color picture tube. The color picture tube differs from the black and white screen in that it is made up of tiny phosphor dots, arranged in groups of three, called *trios*. Each dot of a trio will reflect either red, green, or blue when struck by an electron of the particular color signal. There are almost 600,000 of these tiny dots on the average color screen, so close together that when they receive the three colors in various intensities they tend to blend into the full colors of the scene being broadcast.

Your eyes perform a vital part of the magic of television, blending these color dots into a detailed picture. As you probably know, a picture in a book or a newspaper is really a mass of tiny dots of various intensities, arranged together so that your eye translates them into a detailed reproduction.

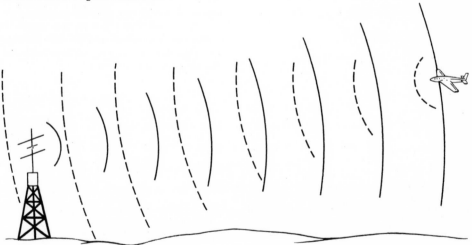

Radar antennas scan the horizon, sending out short radio waves. When the waves hit an object they bounce back to a receiving screen. The time elapsed determines the distance of the object.

The television systems just described are those now in use. But television is still in a pioneering stage, insofar as its engineering development is concerned There is great progress ahead in all fields of electronics; and it offers wonderful opportunities for all who have electrical engineering ambitions.

Closely allied with radio and television are such detection devices as radar and sonar. These are electronic devices used to locate objects and determine their direction and distance from the observation point.

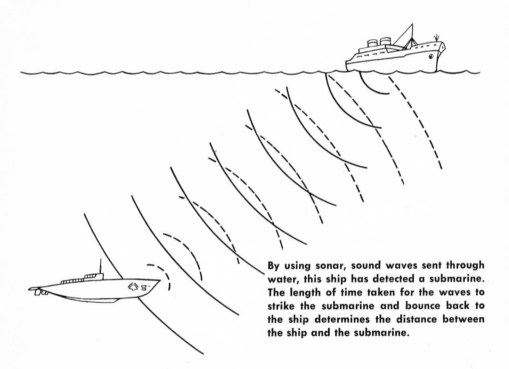

By using sonar, sound waves sent through water, this ship has detected a submarine. The length of time taken for the waves to strike the submarine and bounce back to the ship determines the distance between the ship and the submarine.

Radar antennas scan the sky or the seacoast in all directions. As they do so, they send out very short radio waves. When these waves hit an object, such as a plane in the sky or a ship on the horizon, those beams striking the plane or ship bounce back to the radar antenna, and form a visible silhouette on the receiving screen. The time it takes for the radar signal to travel from the antenna, hit the plane or ship, and bounce back to the antenna indicates how far away the object is.

Sonar waves are sound waves which are sent through the water from the bottom of a ship or from a submarine. They will detect another submarine by bouncing the sound waves back to the transmitter. The time elapsed shows how far away the submarine is when detected.

If you are interested in electronic developments, you will find new strides recorded almost every day in your newspaper. You can follow these developments further in magazines available at your newsstands or in your public library.

CHAPTER EIGHT

CHEMICAL ENGINEERING

E VERYTHING in the world is made up of chemical elements. Scientists have discovered and named just over a hundred basic elements. Ninety-two of these exist in nature and combine in various forms to make up the tissues of living things such as animals and plants, and to create mineral matter such as metals and stones, and even the air we breathe. You yourself are, in one sense, a walking, talking bundle of chemicals.

It is not surprising, therefore, to find that chemistry enters into many of the things we do, and that it is an important factor in many of the subjects we study. Today there is hardly a profession or a process in which chemistry does not have some part. The progress that doctors have made in the last hundred years in keeping people healthy and in extending their useful lives is due almost entirely to chemical discoveries. A modern farmer can grow five times as much on an acre of poor land as the pioneers could grow on virgin soil— because of chemical improvements in the seeds he plants and because of the fertilizers which increase the yield of his crops. Chemistry has given us artificial fibers, such as nylon, and various kinds of multiple-use plastics. The gasoline used for auto and truck fuel, the petroleum used in transportation and heating, and the paints and varnishes used on houses, buildings and furnishings, are all products of chemistry. The crowning achievement of scientific research thus far—the creation of atomic energy—involves chemical reactions in the complicated application of this power to atomic engines.

But the wide world of chemistry must be reduced to the narrower field of the chemical engineer. The best way to accomplish this is to begin with a practical example.

Petroleum is a heavy black liquid formed deep in the earth by chemical action on decaying animal and vegetable matter that once lived and grew on the earth in prehistoric times. This chemical action took place over millions of years. The crude oil that we call petroleum is a complicated mixture of hydrogen and carbon—not just ordinary hydrogen and carbon, but many kinds of hydrocarbon molecules made up of different arrangements of hydrogen atoms and carbon atoms. Each of these different hydrocarbon molecules has different properties,

PETROLEUM REFINING

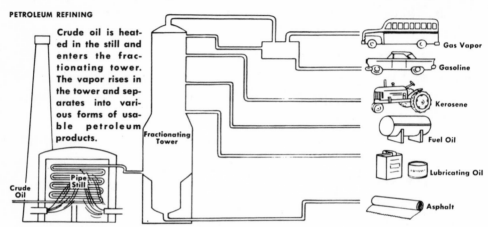

Crude oil is heated in the still and enters the fractionating tower. The vapor rises in the tower and separates into various forms of usable petroleum products.

Fractionating Tower

Pipe Still

Crude Oil

Gas Vapor

Gasoline

Kerosene

Fuel Oil

Lubricating Oil

Asphalt

including differences in weight and differences in the temperatures at which they reach the boiling point.

Petroleum may be broken down into a number of products, ranging from gasoline to heavy engine grease, by the relatively simple process of heating the crude petroleum in a tall tower under high pressure until the liquid turns into gases which collect at various levels in the tower (because of different weights and boiling temperatures). As the gases collect (the lightest ones at the top, and so on) they turn back into liquids which range from gasoline to fuel oil, to kerosene, to very heavy oils and finally to asphalt.

A better way to separate these products is by the chemical process called *catalytic cracking*. A catalyst, as we learn early in the study of chemistry, is something that speeds up or slows down a chemical action without in itself being changed by the chemical process. For instance, the refining of petroleum into various products may be speeded up, and achieved at lower temperatures, if hydrogen is added to the crude petroleum and the mixture is heated in the presence of a catalyst. This catalyst may be one of several metals. The metal is not changed in composition, but the petroleum and hydrogen are changed into gasoline, oil, paraffin and the many other products obtained from petroleum.

A chemist could do this in a laboratory quite easily with relatively simple equipment. But he could work with small quantities only, and the laboratory conditions would not indicate the difficulties which would be encountered under actual manufacturing conditions. Working out such problems is not the job of the laboratory chemist—the research scientist—but of the chemical engineer. For the chemical engineer has a good chemical background and *also* knows the engineering problems involved in making large quantities of the products developed in research laboratories.

The first thing the chemical engineer will do is determine the amount of gasoline and other products to be refined in the new plant. This amount will depend upon the market for these products, and the available supplies of petroleum and hydrogen and catalytic metals

DIAGRAM OF PLANNING STAGES IN BUILDING A PETROLEUM REFINERY

Planning

Scale Model

Full-size Plant

Pilot Model

(plus the amount of money the company has to invest in the new plant and to maintain the necessary labor to operate it).

Next the chemical engineer will construct a small scale model, which doesn't work, but which will tell him many things about how many building materials, pipes, pumps, vats, tanks, etc. will be needed to construct the actual plant.

After the small scale model, he builds a pilot plant. This will be a large working model, not nearly as large as the final plant will be, but complete in all working details so that a quantity of petroleum may actually be refined in it. Operating the pilot plant will uncover many problems which must be solved before the real plant is built. For instance, the engineer might discover that his pilot model refines petroleum for only a little while, then fails because the metal being used for a catalyst is not doing its work properly. This might be traced to a chemical in the pipe compound which is used to seal and lubricate the sections of pipe where they are joined together. Substituting another kind of chemical in the compound might be the solution to this particular problem.

Only when the pilot plant is operating with complete efficiency does the chemical engineer begin to supervise the construction of the full-sized plant. But the work of the chemical engineer goes on after the plant is constructed and is in full operation. There are always tests of the product to be made, there are always failures which call for tracking down the trouble, and there are always changes in requirements for the finished product that call for changes in the manufacturing methods and for changes in the plant itself.

Many of the structures which chemical engineers call plants do not look at all like manufacturing plants to us. They may appear to be nothing but a strange collection of pipes and columns and tanks and stairways and catwalks erected in the open air. But these *are* manufacturing plants, even though they do not have walls and windows and offices. They are so built because much chemical manufacturing needs complete ventilation in order to prevent the build-up of dangerous gases within the walls of a building.

We find chemical engineers busy at work in the industries which produce metals, rubber, plastics, paints and varnishes, glass, soap and insecticides.

The paper on which this book is printed and all the thousands of other paper products we use are products of chemical engineering. Most paper is made from a combination of wood chips and rags which are digested in chemical solutions that dissolve all resins, dyes and other substances, leaving pure cellulose fiber. This cellulose pulp is bleached and washed. Other chemicals then are added to make the paper less porous, so that it will hold ink marks instead of absorbing them as blotting paper does. Still other chemicals are added to make the paper opaque—that is, so that you cannot see through it and so be confused by the printed words appearing backwards on the other side.

The modern food industry offers great opportunities to the chemical engineer. Our breakfast foods, dairy products, canned and frozen foods, smoked and cured meats, all undergo chemical action at some point in their processing. And chemical engineers are now on the edge of one of the most important discoveries in food preservation in man's history—a chemical process involving the use of irradiation with gamma rays that will keep meats fresh for months without refrigeration! Even in this day of careful refrigeration, hundreds of persons die each year because of poisonous bacteria that enter the cells of meat exposed for only a short time to excessive warmth.

Many artificial foods come from the chemist's laboratory. Fruit-flavored gelatins are chemical in nature, including their flavor. This does not mean they are not good for us, since we must not forget that everything in the world is chemical.

The making of cheese from milk is a chemical process. Oleomargarine, a butter substitute, can be made chemically from vegetable oils taken from corn, soybeans, cottonseeds and other plants.

Do you like sugar? You probably wouldn't have liked the kind of sugar that was available to your great-grandparents. It was gray and lumpy, and it was apt to ferment and turn sour after a time. The sugar we use is chemically refined, whitened and dried into smooth-flowing crystals that will stay fresh as long as it is kept dry. All sugar used to come from sugar cane, but today much sugar is chemically extracted and refined from sugar beets.

Salt is pure sodium chloride, a natural compound dug from underground mines or refined from sea water. But although nothing is added to salt (except, in some cases, potassium iodide), it does have to go through considerable chemical refining before it is boxed for table use.

Examples of how chemical engineering enters our daily lives are endless; literally endless, because something new is added to the field every day.

Perhaps you would like to have some fun making some harmless but useful chemical compounds yourself, using chemicals you can buy from your druggist or from a chemical supply house.

Since you are probably quite seriously interested in engineering as a career if you've read this far, let's take up some serious, usable compounds rather than making the parlor-magic kind of chemical mixtures you can find in any book devoted only to that sort of thing.

First of all, perhaps you'd like to amaze your family with some all-purpose, quick-setting glue, good for all kinds of repair jobs. It's very simple: You just mix equal quantities of ordinary rubber cement and shellac (any kind or color). You can get a small bottle of rubber cement at the stationery counter in the ten-cent store, and the shellac can be purchased there also if there doesn't happen to be a can of shellac in your garage or workshop. This household cement will hold together such materials as metal, glass, plastic and other substances that ordinary glue sometimes fails to hold. When you first mix the two ingredients, it is a mixture rather than a chemical compound. The chemical action takes place as the rubber cement and the shellac dry together to form a hard bond that is stronger than the pieces joined. Be sure to keep a tight cover on this mixture when it is not in use, otherwise it will harden in the container.

Your mother will be amazed at your chemical abilities if you mix her a large bottle of hand lotion that will be as good, and possibly better, than the kind she buys. You can buy the ingredients from your neighborhood druggist for less than a dollar. Ask him for 2½ ounces of diglycol stearate, ¼ ounce of borax and 1 pint of gum tragacanth solution.

At home, start with two quarts of water in a pan big enough to contain the water with room to spare. The borax is first added to the water, followed by the diglycol stearate. The mixture is then heated until the added ingredients have melted. Then take a big spoon and mix it as rapidly as you can until it is milky in color and even in consistency. After that you can slow down, but still mixing, until the lotion is almost cool. Then add the gum tragacanth solution. Finally, mix in just a teaspoon of your mother's favorite perfume. Pour the solution into a bottle (find a fancy one if you can), and present your mother (or sister or girl friend) with one of the smoothest hand lotions she has ever used, and one that will leave her hands smelling faintly of her favorite odor.

An unusually effective silver polish which will do its work rapidly and yet will not scratch fine silver can be made from the following ingredients:

Fullers earth	1½ pounds
Sodium carbonate (soda ash)	½ ounce
Trisodium phosphate	½ ounce
Diglycol stearate	¼ pound
Water	2¼ pints

The water and diglycol stearate are heated together until the wax has melted, and the batch is stirred rapidly until it is even in consistency. The other ingredients are then added and thoroughly mixed to form a smooth paste. There is enough polish in this formula for you to pack it in a number of small glass jars and sell to housewives in your neighborhood for some extra money.

Obviously, putting together mixtures like these won't make you a chemical engineer, but as you make these products in small quantities you will begin to have a better understanding of some of the problems faced by the chemical engineer who must erect plants and equipment in which millions of such products are made and packaged every month.

CHAPTER NINE

ATOMIC ENERGY AND SOLAR ENERGY

WE have traced engineering's development from the crude flint tool makers to modern times. We have seen some of the marvels which engineering has created for man. And not only has engineering created wonderful buildings and bridges and machines for man, but it has also made man's life better, made his labor easier, shortened his working hours and increased his productivity so that he now can own more things to share with his family.

There is, however, a dark side of the picture. Throughout history engineering has continued to develop weapons which could kill more men in war, and which have recently made war more horrible than ever by including the civilian population among the victims of war, together with the soldiers and sea fighters on either side. On the other hand, it can be argued that wars have inspired engineers to make improvements which, when translated into civilian uses after the wars, have advanced civilization.

Suddenly—with the development of the atomic bomb and the even more powerful hydrogen bomb—this balance can no longer be expected to regulate itself. The world has become uncomfortably small for world wars—and its weapons have become too powerful. We are in a situation which might be compared to a few men locked together in a small cellar—each of them armed with a hand grenade. None, unless he were insane, would want to throw his hand grenade for fear he too would be killed in the explosion. So it is today with the major nations of the world—each possesses atomic and hydrogen bombs capable of widespread destruction—but each knows, also, that other nations possess similar bombs with which to retaliate. The first atomic bomb used in World War II killed 66,000 persons. The much more powerful hydrogen bomb could destroy a city of 3,000,000 persons. Yet, the greatest hope for a peaceful world lies in the fact that such devastating weapons have been developed for our national defense.

There is further hope for peace in the fact that science and engineering have pointed to ways by which nations can now peacefully, easily and more cheaply achieve what they attempted to gain by waging war. We know now that by applying the proper engineering methods, no people need go hungry. The achievements of agricultural engineering in the United States are an example. While our country has fewer farmers in relation to its whole population than any other country in the world, these relatively few farmers produce an embarrassing amount of food—so much that the United States has a serious surplus food problem.

The less heavily industrialized nations of the world, given some help from the more technologically advanced countries, can replace human and animal labor with electric power derived from dams. These nations can even be assisted to build atomic energy plants.

Atomic energy, one of the newest sources of power in the world, could advance such a country within a few years to a point where it could enjoy the benefits of the Industrial Revolution, which were achieved in England and the United States only after hundreds of years.

The earliest type of atomic bomb—the fission bomb—explodes because of a rapid, runaway chain reaction of splitting atoms.

On the other hand, when the same chain reaction is controlled by various means and is not permitted to get out of hand, no explosion occurs. Only terrific heat is generated. Of course, engineers know what to do with heat.

That is exactly what engineers did when they built the famous atomic submarine *Nautilus*. While the *Nautilus* is said to be atomic powered, its engines are modern steam turbines, operated by steam created by the heat given off by the atomic reactor. Using the same principles, atomic ships, atomic railroad locomotives, atomic airplanes, perhaps even atomic automobiles can be built. One drawback to an atomic family automobile, of course, is that the atomic energy plant must be heavily shielded to protect people from harmful radiation. Thus far, this necessity results in atomic energy plants which are too bulky for such uses.

But atomic energy is already at work in the world, and the use of this new source of power is increasing every year. In the same way that atomic energy is used to produce steam for turbines, it is also made to turn dynamos to produce electricity. There are many industrial processes which require extremely high temperatures—for instance, the making of artificial diamonds which are to be used for cutting hard materials in industry. Atomic energy can supply heat high enough to produce artificial diamonds which are as hard as natural diamonds, hitherto the hardest substance in the world.

Engineers have suggested the use of atomic energy in rocket engines instead of the conventional rocket fuels. These rockets would eject atomic particles at tremendous speeds, providing the thrust for the rocket planes.

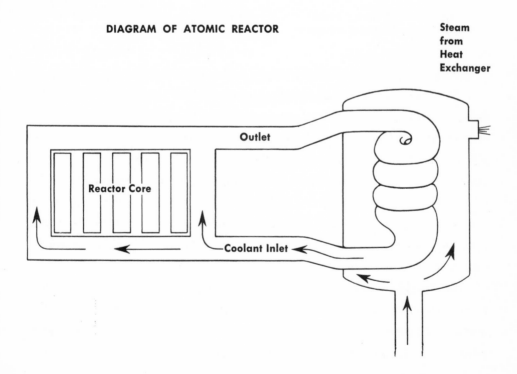

DIAGRAM OF ATOMIC REACTOR

Steam
from
Heat
Exchanger

Outlet

Reactor Core

Coolant Inlet

This is a powerful servant man has unleashed in atomic energy! Seven pounds of uranium in the heart of a reactor in the first civilian power plant, erected in Shippingport, Pennsylvania, in 1954, produce as much working energy every month as might be obtained from 20,000 pounds of coal per month. But the uranium in the reactor does not have to be replaced each month; it will go on producing heat for a long, long time.

The energy obtained from 7 pounds of uranium per month is equal to the energy obtained from 20,000 pounds of coal per month.

Some of the plans of scientists and engineers for the future use of atomic energy sound almost as if they had originated in science fiction! They have seriously suggested that we can make our world's climate more pleasant by using atomic energy to blast the ice caps off the North and South Poles! They think it would be possible to change the path of the earth around the sun, and to change the angle at which it revolves, in order to improve the climate—eliminating the worst cold of winter and the extreme heat of midsummer. It would also be possible, say the scientists and engineers, to make some of our neighboring planets suitable for human habitation.

So quickly does the engineering picture change, and so dependent is the engineer on energy in the best available form, that today's engineering students must have a working knowledge of forms of energy which are still in the developmental stage.

SOLAR ENERGY

While atomic energy is important to tomorrow's engineer, another and more simple form of energy will also be in wide use—in fact it is already in use in many parts of the world. That is the prime source of all energy in the world—the sun.

Borrow a small magnifying glass if you can—or buy an inexpensive one at the variety store. Crumple a piece of cleansing tissue and take it outside on a hot sunshiny day. Put the tissue on the sidewalk, and hold the magnifying glass over it in such a position that it will concentrate the sun's rays on the tissue. In a very short time the tissue will start to smolder and smoke, and finally it will burst into flame.

What has happened? Heat waves reach us from the sun together with light waves. But even on the hottest days, the heat would not be intense enough to set paper afire. The magnifying glass, acting as a lens, bends the heat waves and concentrates them on one spot of the paper, intensifying the heat to the point where the paper bursts into flame.

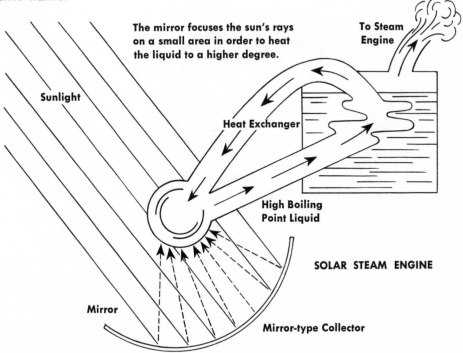

The mirror focuses the sun's rays on a small area in order to heat the liquid to a higher degree.

To Steam Engine

Sunlight

Heat Exchanger

High Boiling Point Liquid

SOLAR STEAM ENGINE

Mirror

Mirror-type Collector

You can measure the increase in heat provided by the concentration of heat waves through the magnifying glass. Take a bottle cap or anything else that will hold a small quantity of water. Now take a bulb thermometer and take the temperature of the water, which should roughly correspond to the temperature of the outside air. Fix your magnifying glass so it will concentrate the sun's rays over the container of water for several minutes. Now take the temperature of the water. You will find it 15 to 20 degrees hotter.

You will not be able to get the water in your bottle cap to boil and produce steam. But you could if you had a large enough lens and bright metal reflectors to help gather sun rays to pass through the lens. In fact, simple devices like this are used in Egypt, and in other hot countries of the world, to create steam which operates steam engines. On cloudy days, of course, this kind of solar energy engine will not function. It is not a reliable or a very efficient operation even under the best circumstances.

This is an experiment in solar heating that you can try yourself.

But on cloudy days, when we are not getting direct rays of the sun, solar energy is still reaching the earth. You can trap that energy on a cloudy day in this way: Take a deep box, open on one side, and paint the inside black. Fasten a thermometer to the bottom of the inside, and put a sheet of glass over the open side. Now prop the box in such a position that it faces the sun, even though the sun is not visible. During the day, watch how the thermometer reading creeps up as your solar "hot box" gathers heat from the solar rays. If the box were white, or some other light color, it would reflect the heat rays back out of the box and the thermometer would not register much of a heat gain. But black absorbs heat, rather than reflects it. You will find that your "hot box" retains its heat long after the sun has gone down and the evening air has become chilly.

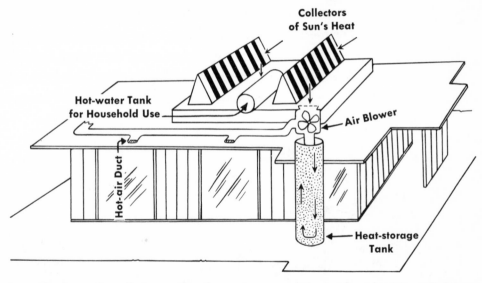

In a solar house the collectors gather the sun's rays and the resultant heat is carried to a gravel-filled storage tank. The heat is circulated through hot-air ducts by a blower.

In the southern United States, many homes are heated in a similar way. Black metal plates and sheets of glass cover the roofs of such homes, gathering heat from the sun on winter days. The heat is released slowly, and lasts during the night. Next day the heat supply is replenished by the sun, even on cloudy days. Such heating plants are efficient only in regions where winters are mild. In the northern states, where winters are colder, the heat loss would be too rapid for a home to be heated comfortably.

The kinds of uses for solar energy we have described thus far are fairly primitive, and involve the use of *molecular motion* set up by heat. In other words, the molecules of heated air are extremely active, while the molecules in very cold air move much more slowly. Not all of the ways in which solar energy is used today are new. Three hundred years before the birth of Christ, the Greeks used huge concave mirrors (serving as lenses) to concentrate the sun's rays on enemy ships and set them afire. Greek priests used the sun's rays to create heated air which, when released, turned delicately balanced mechanisms. With such devices they caused temple doors to open with the rising of the morning sun, and they caused the statues of their gods to turn and follow the path of the sun across the sky.

Modern experiments consist of taking these ancient devices and multiplying their effectiveness many times over. By using as many as 3,500 small mirrors, solar furnaces which produce temperatures as high as 7,500 degrees Fahrenheit have been built! These furnaces

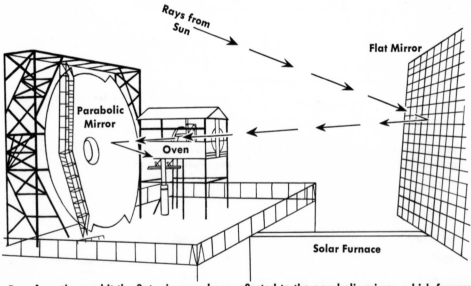

Rays from the sun hit the flat mirror and are reflected to the parabolic mirror, which focuses them onto a single hot spot in the oven.

have been used to melt metals into alloys, and have been found very useful since ordinary high-temperature furnaces often introduce impurities which render the alloys less effective than when a solar furnace is used.

But the capturing, intensifying and storing of the sun's heat is not the only way solar energy may be harnessed. For solar energy may be converted into electrical energy. In this procedure solar rays are passed into certain materials, such as selenium and silicon, and some of the electrons in the material are completely knocked out of their regular orbits by the solar rays and are set free. By connecting electrical leads to different electrical potentials in the material, current is made to flow. Such devices are called solar batteries, and are already in use in some parts of the United States, operating telephone exchange lines in rural areas. The batteries store enough surplus energy during the day to operate the lines at night when the sun is down.

There is still another possible use of solar energy. It may be captured in chemical form, as in the radium-treated hands and dials of a clock or watch that is luminous in the dark. Some engineers say that by so treating ceilings and walls, we shall some day light our homes with captured solar energy. The fourth way in which we shall most certainly use solar energy in the future remains for scientists and engineers to develop. That is, the use of solar energy to completely rearrange the atoms in a molecule, in the same way that we rearrange atoms through nuclear fission. We know this can be done with solar energy because growing plants do just this. Every growing thing in the plant world absorbs solar radiation, and by means of chlorophyll, converts water and carbon dioxide into carbohydrates and oxygen. This kind of use of solar energy has not yet been duplicated by man. But let us not forget that the old saying, "What man dreams of, he can do," has often proven true.

CHAPTER TEN

SPACE AND ROCKET ENGINEERING

BY WILLY LEY

Like some other branches of engineering, *rocket engineering* began as an art. The earliest type of rocket—the type we now call the skyrocket or the Fourth of July rocket—was invented in China around the year A.D. 1200. By 1255 the device was mentioned in Europe; the report of the new device must have traveled very fast for its time.

Most likely only a description, not an actual rocket, made the trip, so that the people in Europe had to "invent" it all over again. They knew what this new device did and they had heard that it was a tube filled with a new substance consisting of charcoal, sulfur and saltpeter. They probably had been told that it had a shaft like an arrow. Now they had to build it and make it work.

The method which was evolved in Europe is known to us because early makers of fireworks wrote it down carefully for their apprentices. First the powder was mixed—about 60 per cent of saltpeter, 25 per cent of charcoal and 15 per cent of sulfur—and then it was hammered into a cardboard tube, a little at a time. Then a guiding stick was tied to the finished rocket. The fireworks masters wrote down that the stick should be seven times as long as the rocket. As for the thickness of the guiding stick, it was right if the charged rocket tube just balanced the weight of the stick when the assembled rocket was placed on a knife-edge just below the lower end of the tube.

From about 1500 until 1800 there was no change in this process of making rockets. One artisan might be more skillful than another one, but they all used the same method. But soon after 1800 the English captain (later general) William Congreve introduced a few innovations. He did not use a mallet any more for compressing the powder, but a press. And he learned that the danger of self-ignition while loading, an ever present hazard, could be reduced by moistening the powder with alcohol.

In spite of Congreve's contribution to the art, real rocket engineering did not come into existence until about 1925. In 1919 Professor Robert H. Goddard, a New England physicist, had published a very technical treatise in which he gave mathematical formulae for calculating rocket performance. Four years later an Austrian mathematician —he knew nothing of Goddard then, since both wrote their works during the first World War—by the name of Hermann Oberth had published another book in which he not only gave the mathematics for calculating what one wanted to find out but even described several liquid-fuel rockets he wanted to build.

The two books laid the foundation for modern rocket engineering. Having these books an engineer could calculate in advance what he wanted to accomplish (or what he might be able to accomplish) and go on from there. The first man actually to build a liquid-fuel rocket was Professor Goddard himself: his first successful liquid-fuel rocket rose 180 feet into the air from Auburn, Massachusetts, in March, 1926.

In fact, Professor Goddard—though a physicist by training— might well be called the first rocket engineer. For several years thereafter he continued to experiment with various types of rockets (all with liquid fuels) and even simple guidance systems. His crowning achievement was a shot fired to an altitude of 7500 feet in 1935 from the Mescalero Ranch near Roswell, New Mexico.

But by that time several other early rocket engineers had begun their careers. In Germany the Society for Space Travel, founded in 1927, had begun experimenting with liquid-fuel rockets in 1929. By 1931 the Society had progressed to a respectable number of vertical shots to about 2/3 of a mile, with parachute recovery for the rockets so that they could be used over again. And, beginning in 1929, the

Russians had also embarked on a rocket research program. In 1935, when Professor Goddard reached 7500 feet, the Russian team succeeded in sending a rocket up to almost six miles. In the following year the German Army, which had gone in for rocket research and had hired Wernher von Braun away from the Society for Space Travel, sent two rockets to altitudes of a little less than 7000 feet.

By 1940 the German Army dominated the field. The Russians had discontinued rocket research in 1939 while Professor Goddard had been forced to give up for lack of funds.

But at the same time the armed services of several countries, notably England, the United States and Germany, began a new line of investigation: namely that of creating solid-fuel rockets which could be fired in the field like field artillery, or which could be fired from shipboard against shore targets, or from airplanes against other airplanes or against targets on the ground.

These new solid-fuel rockets differed from the solid-fuel fireworks which had existed for centuries in using smokeless powders of various kinds as propellants. As a result of the second World War the profession of rocket engineer was established, even though the missile programs of the large nations were still in the future.

Before we can start describing how the various kinds of rockets are constructed, it might be necessary to explain the distinction between a rocket and a missile.

The term "rocket" refers to the propulsion of the device. In a rocket the fuel and the oxygen to burn this fuel are *both* carried along so that the rocket is independent of the outer air. It does *not* need the oxygen of the atmosphere to burn the fuel, as does a piston engine, a turbojet or even a ramjet. It does not matter what the rocket is supposed to accomplish, whether it is to throw a warhead to a target, or just carry instruments to high altitudes, or put a satellite into an orbit. The term "rocket", to repeat, refers to the method of propulsion.

The term "missile," on the other hand, refers to the purpose of the device. A missile is used to hit something, in the air, on the ground, or on the seas. It does not matter how it is propelled. It can be rocket propelled like a Jupiter missile, or it can be propelled by a turbojet like the Snark missile. It could even be propelled by a piston engine, though there happens to be no missile in existence which actually is.

Though the purpose of a missile is to hit something, the military make a finer distinction. They do not call something that is just fired at an enemy target, for example a shell, or a bazooka rocket, a missile. To the military the term "missile" means a weapon which can be guided; its flight path can still be influenced *after* it has been fired to make sure that it will strike the target.

Now a solid-fuel rocket consists of three main parts. The nose is the warhead or, more generally, the *payload*. The payload is the reason for the shot; it is the payload which must be transported from one point to another. Behind the payload there is, if the rocket is a missile, the compartment containing the guidance equipment.

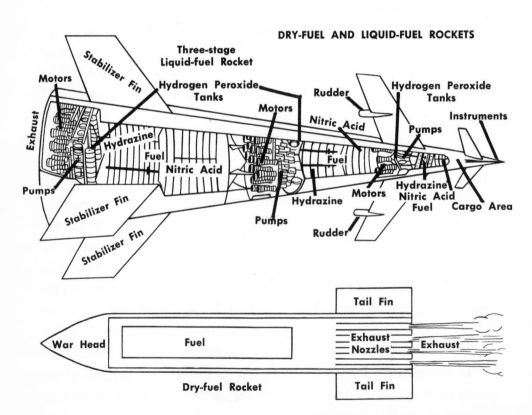

DRY-FUEL AND LIQUID-FUEL ROCKETS

Then follows the main portion of the rocket as far as size is concerned. It is the cylindrical section which holds the *fuel charge*. It is normally a steel tube which has been charged with the substance that is to be burned for propulsion. Just how the charge is placed inside this compartment—it is somewhat misleadingly called the "rocket motor" —depends mostly on the purpose of the rocket. If the rocket has to have a very short burning time (for example, the bazooka rocket must have stopped burning before it leaves the launching tube, otherwise the soldier firing it would get a backblast in his face) the propelling charge burns *unrestricted*. This means that the charge, which has the shape of a thick-walled tube (or of several tubes), burns from the outside in, from the inside out and also from both ends, so that it is consumed as fast as possible.

In bigger rockets the charge is usually *restricted*. This means that the propelling charge fits the walls of the rocket motor and it burns only from the center hole outward. Even then the burning is quite rapid; there are rockets in which the propellant charge weighs 1200 pounds but these 1200 pounds are consumed in about three seconds. One type of the restricted burning rocket has been nicknamed "cigarette burner." The charge of such a rocket has no center hole and burns, inside its tube, from one end to the other, about the way a cigarette burns. These "cigarette burners" give thrust over a longer period, but the thrust is weaker than that of the other two types. "Cigarette burners" are usually used as take-off help for airplanes.

The tail end of the rocket, finally, is the *exhaust nozzle*. In the exhaust nozzle the combustion gases of the burning fuel charge are first compressed and then they go through a widening portion of the exhaust nozzle. If the nozzle has been built properly the exhaust gases emerge at a high rate of speed. The faster they emerge, the more powerful the thrust.

As has been mentioned, there are several types of solid fuels. One very modern type consists of a kind of synthetic rubber into which a substance that gives off oxygen has been incorporated. Other solid fuel charges are the so-called "double-base powders." They are made by soaking gun cotton, a high explosive, in nitroglycerin, another high explosive (hence the name "double base"), and adding substances which make this mixture turn into a kind of hard gelatin.

All bombardment rockets have always been solid-fuel rockets and, as time goes on, more and more of the missiles are becoming solid-fuel rockets, too. The reason is simple: a solid-fuel rocket, once made, is a packaged unit, very much like a rifle cartridge. It can be stored, ready for action, and if the need for action arises the rocket is ready.

Solid-fuel rockets are much simpler to handle than liquid-fuel rockets, but they have the main drawback that they can do only what they have been built to do. If a solid-fuel charge has been designed to give a thrust of 2000 pounds for ten seconds, it will do that. But nothing else. It will not be able to produce 1000 pounds of thrust for twenty seconds, or 4000 pounds of thrust for 5 seconds.

With liquid fuels the story is different, but let us first have a look at a liquid-fuel rocket. As in the solid-fuel job, the nose is the payload. Then comes the guidance compartment. After this are the fuel tanks, two of them. One holds the fuel proper which may be kerosene, gasoline, ethyl alcohol or some more unusual substance such as aniline or unsymmetrical dimethyl hydrazine (the fuel for the second stage of the Vanguard rocket). The other tank usually holds liquid oxygen which is the *oxidizer* for the fuel. A number of rockets do not use liquid oxygen, but instead use nitric acid, a liquid rich in oxygen.

Below the fuel tanks there is a compartment which holds the following: the fuel pumps, often an auxiliary fuel tank (because the fuel pumps run on a different fuel from the rocket itself), the pipes which distribute the fuel and the oxidizer so that they enter the rocket motor in the proper places and, finally, the rocket motor itself. The rocket motor consists of injection nozzles for the fuel and oxidizer, the combustion chamber where the burning takes place and the exhaust nozzle. Sometimes rocket engineers refer to the rocket motor *plus* fuel pipes, fuel pumps, etc. as the rocket engine.

Why are liquid fuels better for some purposes?

Well, in a solid-fuel rocket the rocket motor must be strong enough to withstand the pressure produced by the combustion gases. And in a solid-fuel rocket the rocket motor is the biggest part of the whole. In the liquid-fuel rocket the rocket motor also must be strong enough to withstand the combustion pressure. But here the rocket motor is comparatively small, the large fuel tanks do not need to be pressurized and can, therefore, be light. The necessary pressure for feeding the liquids into the rocket motor is produced by the fuel pumps. All this means that a liquid-fuel rocket has less dead weight. And then the liquid-fuel rocket can do what the solid-fuel rocket cannot do. If you let the fuel pumps run a bit faster, they will feed more fuel and oxidizer into the rocket motor and the thrust will go up. Or you can slow down the fuel pumps a bit, and the thrust will be less, but the fuel will last for a longer period. Moreover you can shut a liquid-fuel motor off completely if you want to and re-ignite it later, while a solid-fuel charge will keep burning until it is completely consumed.

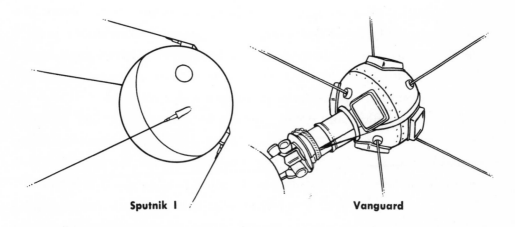

Sputnik I   Vanguard

The first of the man-made satellites was Sputnik I. It was launched by the Russians on October 4, 1957 and fell to Earth three months later. The smallest of all the satellites is Vanguard, launched by the Americans on March 17, 1958. It is expected to continue circling the Earth for about 200 years.

For this reason all space activities will stay with liquid fuels. So will all manned flight by rocket, whether it goes far out into space or skims just above the outer layers of our atmosphere. And, because of the fine control needed, it is likely that, among the missiles, the intercontinental ballistic missile will remain liquid fueled.

It is typical of all rockets that their flight times are much longer than their propulsion times. An intercontinental missile which will need about 50 minutes to span an ocean will burn for only 3-1/3 minutes. A rocket putting an artificial satellite into an orbit around the earth will burn for a total of, at most, five minutes. What counts, in all cases, is not the duration of burning, or the duration of flight. What counts is the velocity only. A rocket which attains a maximum velocity of one mile per second is a missile with a range of about 200 miles. A rocket which attains a maximum velocity of two miles a second is a missile with a range of about 900 miles. Four miles a second gives intercontinental range and five miles a second puts a satellite into orbit.

But we have talked so much about the various rockets that we have neglected to talk about the rocket engineers. What kind of people do conceive, design and build the rockets?

Actually quite a number of different sciences are involved. The fuels are clearly in the domain of the chemist. All calculations involve large amounts of mathematics, so there are mathematicians in the rocket and missile field. Since space activities involve space there are some astronomers in the field. And since space activities will soon involve people, pilots and crews, there is now a special branch of medicine which is called space medicine and which is, of course, investigated by physicians. Finally, there are a number of physicists working in the field. One of their duties is to design the necessary instruments.

But the bulk of all the people who conceive and design rockets and missiles are engineers, various kinds of engineers. The rocket motor, the fuel pump and all that goes with it will usually be designed by a mechanical engineer. The overall shape of the rocket is likely to be up to an aeronautical engineer, especially the shape of the wings, if any, and of the tail fins and other control surfaces. But the vast field of tracking the missile, of guiding it or, in the case of artificial satellites and research rockets, of *telemetering* (as the automatic broadcasting of information gathered by rocket-borne instruments is called) is clearly up to the electronics engineer. That is his field and there is no reason why the fuel chemist or the space doctor have to understand it.

It is always taken for granted that the man who wishes to specialize in space medicine must be a doctor before he can begin to specialize. Strangely enough this is not taken for granted in the case of the engineer. But the same reasoning applies. The person who wants to specialize in rocket engineering must first be an engineer of some sort before he can specialize. For example, you cannot just study the design of a transmitter which, let us say, produces a radio signal for tracking the missile. In order to understand such a transmitter, and then to design a new one, you first have to be an all-around electronics engineer. The same applies to the mechanical engineer who designs the rocket motor, and to the aeronautical engineer who designs the control surfaces and determines where they should be attached to the missile.

It is possible that some time in the future, an engineering college may decide to teach a special course in rocket engineering. The students in such a course will have to learn a great many things which they did not think would pertain to rocket engineering. In the meantime, however, the rocket engineer will be a person with engineering training who decided to specialize in this new and exciting field.

APPENDIX

There is at least one college of engineering in each state of the U. S. In Canada, engineering is taught at 19 universities, 11 of which offer engineering degrees. Your school librarian has pamphlets and other materials which will help you in selecting a college.

These are typical requirements for admission to most engineering colleges:

English	3	units
Social Studies	1	unit
Algebra	1½	units
Plane Geometry	1	unit
Physics or Chemistry	1	unit
General Science	1	unit
Additional work in the above subjects	3	units
Other subjects	3½	units
Total	15	units

These represent the average *minimum* requirements for entrance. Many engineering colleges require more units. A unit is a full year's credit for a subject. Be sure to check the requirements of the particular college in which you are interested while you still are in high school.

Pamphlet material which will give you career guidance in the engineering field is available from the institutions listed below. Most of this material is free. All of these sources prefer that requests for the material come to them from a teacher, and be written on school stationery. Your teacher will be glad to help you obtain the material you want.

American Society of Mechanical
Engineers
29 West 39th Street,
New York 18, N. Y.

Bell Aircraft Corporation
P. O. Box 1, Buffalo 5, N. Y.

American Society of Civil Engineers
33 West 39th Street,
New York 18, N. Y.

Engineers' Council for Professional
Development
29 West 39th Street,
New York 18, N. Y.
(Send 25c for pamphlet)

National Society of Professional
Engineers
2029 K Street, N. W.,
Washington, D. C.

New York Life Insurance Company
51 Madison Avenue,
New York 10, N. Y.

General Motors Corporation
GM Technical Center
Box 177, N. End Station,
Detroit 2, Mich.

International Business Machines
Corporation
Department of Information
590 Madison Avenue,
New York 22, N. Y.

Purdue University
Office, University Editor
Room 417,
Engineering Administration Bldg.,
Lafayette, Indiana

Massachusetts Institute of Technology
Director of Admissions
Cambridge, Mass.

Rutgers University
Director of Admissions
New Brunswick, N. J.

Michigan College of Mining
and Technology
Director of College Relations
Houghton, Mich.

Illinois Institute of Technology
Technical Center, Chicago 16, Ill.

American Institute of Mining,
Metallurgical and
Petroleum Engineers
29 West 39th Street,
New York 18, N. Y.

American Institute of
Industrial Engineers
145 North High Street,
Columbus 15, Ohio

Engineering Manpower Commission
29 West 39th Street,
New York 18, N. Y.

Women's Bureau,
United States Department of Labor
Washington 25, D. C.

Engineering Institute of Canada
2050 Mansfield Street,
Montreal 2, Quebec, Canada

INDEX